Materials for the "Say YES to Youth"
Project were funded by a grant
from the Carnegie Foundation to
Detroit Public Library.

BIOMES

OF THE WORLD

VOLUME 5

Mountains

MICHAEL ALLABY

GROLIER
EDUCATIONAL

About This Set

BIOMES OF THE WORLD is a nine-volume set that describes all the major landscapes (biomes) that are found across the Earth. Biomes are large areas of the world where living conditions for plants and animals are broadly similar, so that the vegetation in these locations appears much the same. Each of the books in this set describes one or more of the main biomes: Volume 1: The Polar Regions (tundra, ice cap, and permanent ice); Volume 2: Deserts (desert and semidesert); Volume 3: Oceans (oceans and islands); Volume 4: Wetlands (lakes, rivers, marshes, and estuaries); **Volume 5: Mountains** (mountain and highland); Volume 6: Temperate Forests (boreal coniferous forest or taiga, coastal coniferous forest, broad-leaf and mixed forest, Mediterranean forest and scrub); Volume 7: Tropical Forests (rain forest and monsoon forest); Volume 8: Temperate Grasslands (prairie, steppe, and pampas); Volume 9: Tropical Grasslands (savanna).

The books each have three sections. The first describes the geographical location of the biome, its climate, and other physical features that make it the way it is. The second section describes the plants and animals that inhabit the biome and the ways in which they react to each other. The final section of each book deals with the threats to the biome and what is being done to reduce these. An introduction in Volume 1 includes a map showing all the biomes described in this set, and a map showing all the countries of the world.

Throughout the pages of this set there are diagrams explaining the processes described in the text, artwork depictions of animals and plants, diagrams showing ecosystems, and tables. The many color photographs bring each biome to life. At the end of each book there is a glossary explaining the meaning of technical words used, a list of other sources of reference (books and websites), followed by an index to all the volumes in the set.

Published 1999 by Grolier Educational,
Danbury, CT 06816

This edition published exclusively for the school and library market

Planned and produced by
Andromeda Oxford Limited,
11–13 The Vineyard, Abingdon, Oxon
OX14 3PX, UK

Project Manager: *Graham Bateman*
Editors: *Jo Newson, Penelope Isaac*
Art Editor and Designer: *Steve McCurdy*
Cartography: *Richard Watts, Tim Williams*
Editorial Assistant: *Marian Dreier*
Picture Manager: *Claire Turner*
Production: *Nicolette Colborne*

Origination by Expo Holdings Sdn Bhd, Malaysia
Printed in Hong Kong

Set ISBN 0-7172-9341-6
Volume 5 ISBN 0-7172-9346-7

Biomes of the world.
    p.   cm.
  Includes indexes.
    Contents: v. 1. Polar regions -- v. 2. Deserts -- v. 3. Oceans -- v. 4. Wetlands -- v. 5. Mountains -- v. 6. Temperate forests -- v. 7. Tropical forests -- v. 8. Temperate grassland -- v. 9. Tropical grassland.
    Summary: In nine volumes, explores each of the earth's major ecological regions, defining important features, animals, and environmental issues.
    ISBN 0-7172-9341-6 (hardcover : set : alk. paper). -- ISBN 0-7172-9346-7 (hardcover : vol. 5 : alk. paper)
    1. Biotic communities--juvenile literature. 2. Life zones--Juvenile literature. 3. Ecology--Juvenile literature. [1. Biotic communities.] I. Grolier Educational (Firm)
  QH541.14.B57   1999
  577--dc21   98-37524
                                              CIP
                                              AC

Contents

The Physical World of Mountains

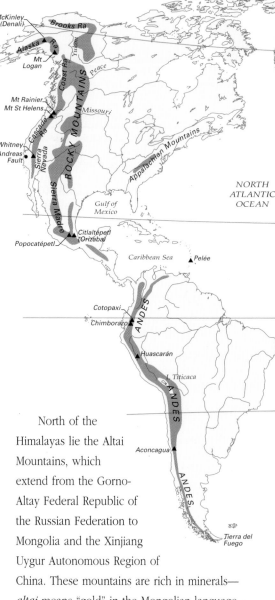

*B*are, *jagged rocks and snow-capped peaks shining brilliantly against a clear blue sky create scenery as dramatic as any the Earth can offer. Mountains inspire us with their beauty. They also remind us of the huge forces that can crumple the surface of the Earth as though it were made of paper, thrusting up mountains miles high in ranges thousands of miles long.*

The highest mountains on Earth are found in the Himalayas, the range that stretches across Asia for about 1,500 miles (2,400 km), from northern Pakistan to China. Jammu and Kashmir, the territory to which both Pakistan and India lay claim, southern Tibet, northern India, the countries of Nepal and Bhutan and, between them, the Indian state of Sikkim, all lie in the Himalayan range. Mount Everest, the highest mountain in the world, is in the Himalayas. Its peak is at 29,028 feet (8,848 m). It is one of more than 30 Himalayan mountains that are more than 25,000 feet (7,620 m) high.

To its west the Himalayan range is bordered by the Karakorum range and, beyond that, by the mountains of Afghanistan. To its north lies the high Tibetan Plateau, which is more than 12,000 feet (3,660 m) above sea level.

North of the Himalayas lie the Altai Mountains, which extend from the Gorno-Altay Federal Republic of the Russian Federation to Mongolia and the Xinjiang Uygur Autonomous Region of China. These mountains are rich in minerals—*altai* means "gold" in the Mongolian language. Mount Belukha, at 15,157 feet (4,620 m), is the highest peak of the Altai.

Far to the west the Ural Mountains mark the boundary between Europe and Asia. They lie along a north–south line 1,640 miles (2,639 km) long, from the borders of the Arctic Ocean, in the far north of Russia, to the Caspian Sea, in Kazakhstan. They are not high mountains, the highest being Narodnaya at 6,214 feet (1,894 m).

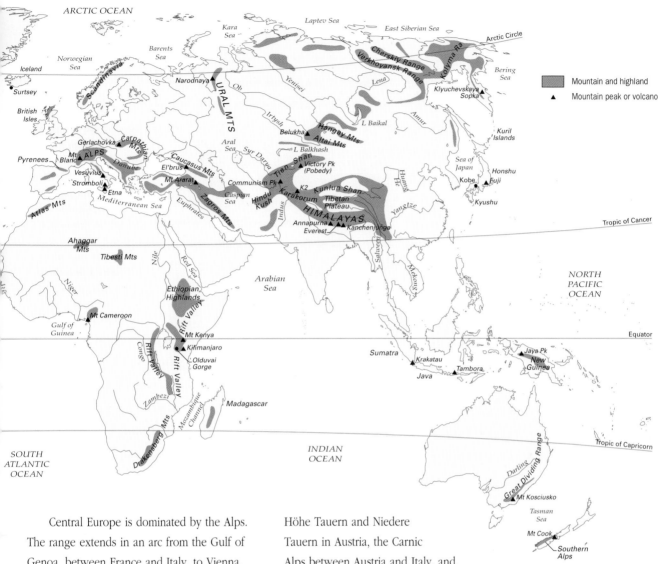

Mountain and highland

▲ Mountain peak or volcano

Central Europe is dominated by the Alps. The range extends in an arc from the Gulf of Genoa, between France and Italy, to Vienna, a distance of about 750 miles (1,200 km). It covers an area of about 92,700 square miles (240,000 sq. km). In fact, the Alps are made up of several mountain ranges, which form two main groups, the western and eastern Alps, separated along a line from the Rhine Valley in Switzerland to Lake Como, Italy. The western Alps are generally higher than the eastern Alps. The highest peak in the Alps is Mont Blanc, in France, at 15,771 feet (4,807 m).

The eastern Alps divide into a number of ranges, including the Bavarian Alps in Germany,

Höhe Tauern and Niedere Tauern in Austria, the Carnic Alps between Austria and Italy, and the Dolomite Alps in Italy.

The Transylvanian Alps in Romania are not, despite their name, part of the Alps, but form the southern end of the Carpathian Mountains. These extend in a semicircle for about 900 miles (1,450 km) through Slovakia, southern Poland, and Romania. There are several peaks more than 8,000 feet (2,440 m) high, but they are not high mountains. The highest is Gerlachovka Peak in Slovakia, at 8,711 feet (2,655 m).

The Rocky Mountains of North America form a system of mountain ranges 2,000 miles

MOUNTAIN RANGES.
There are mountains on every continent. The highest are found in the Himalayan range in Asia. The Andes in South America is the longest range. The Ural Mountains in Russia and Kazakhstan mark the border between Europe and Asia.

(3,200 km) long. They begin in the northwest with the Alaska Range, in southern Alaska, and continue through Canada. In the United States the ranges become wider; the Cascade and Coast Ranges and Sierra Nevada lie to the west of the main range. (*Sierra* is from the Spanish for "saw" and describes a range with jagged peaks, like a toothed blade). In Mexico the Sierra Madre mountains lie to the east and west of the high Mexican Plateau, and in the south the Rockies are linked to the Central American Cordillera.

Mount McKinley, in the Alaska Range, is the highest peak in North America, at 20,321 feet (6,194 m) high. Other high peaks are St Elias, in the St Elias Mountains, on the Canada–United States border, which rises to 18,008 feet (5,489 m), and Popocatépetl, on the Mexican Plateau, which is 17,887 feet (5,452 m) high.

The chain continues in South America as the Andes. It runs the length of the continent, parallel to the western coast, a distance of 4,500 miles (7,240 km). The average elevation throughout the range is about 12,000 feet (3,660 m)—the same as that of the Tibetan Plateau—and there are many high peaks. Aconcagua, in Argentina, is the highest at 22,834 feet (6,960 m) high. Chimborazo, in Ecuador, is 20,703 feet (6,310 m) high.

WRINKLES IN THE SKIN

The Earth is composed of several layers with a common center ("concentric" layers). Soil and rocks form the outermost skin of the solid Earth, but they form only a thin layer, called the crust. Beneath the crust lies the mantle, composed of hot, semimolten rocks, and below that a liquid outer core encloses a solid inner core made from almost pure iron.

It is only at the surface that the Earth is cool. If you were to drill a hole vertically into the crust, the temperature would increase with depth. Miners deep below ground, therefore, work in a warm environment. The rate at which the temperature increases with depth is called the geothermal gradient ("geothermal" describes the heat on the inside of the Earth). This varies from place to place, averaging about 87°F for every mile of depth (30°C per km). Almost all the warmth is produced by the decay of radioactive elements in the rock.

Continental and Oceanic Crust

The crust that lies beneath continents is called continental crust and is on average 19–25 miles (30–40 km) thick. Its upper part consists of rocks with an average density of about 166 pounds per cubic foot (2.66 tonnes per cu. m). Below these, in the lower crust, the density increases to about 187 pounds per cubic foot (3.0 tonnes per cu. m).

The oceanic crust, beneath the oceans, is more complex. It consists of four layers, the uppermost layer consisting of sedimentary rock, and varies from about 3 to 6 miles (5 to 10 km) in thickness. The density of the rocks in the three lower layers is similar to that of the lower continental crust, about 187 pounds per cubic foot (3.0 tonnes per cu. m).

The Mohorovičić Discontinuity

There is a boundary between the base of both continental and oceanic crust and the material beneath. This was discovered by a Croatian

A SECTION THROUGH THE EARTH. The solid rocks at the surface of the Earth form a thin crust beneath which lies the mantle, a much thicker layer of hot, semimolten rocks. Below the mantle the liquid outer core encloses a solid inner core made from almost pure iron.

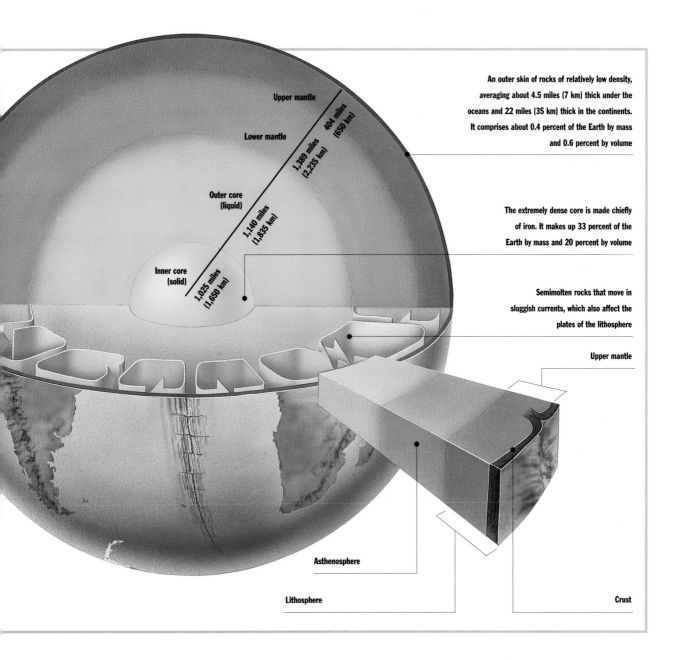

Upper mantle

Lower mantle

404 miles
(650 km)

1,389 miles
(2,235 km)

Outer core
(liquid)

1,140 miles
(1,835 km)

Inner core
(solid)

1,025 miles
(1,650 km)

An outer skin of rocks of relatively low density, averaging about 4.5 miles (7 km) thick under the oceans and 22 miles (35 km) thick in the continents. It comprises about 0.4 percent of the Earth by mass and 0.6 percent by volume

The extremely dense core is made chiefly of iron. It makes up 33 percent of the Earth by mass and 20 percent by volume

Semimolten rocks that move in sluggish currents, which also affect the plates of the lithosphere

Upper mantle

Asthenosphere

Lithosphere

Crust

seismologist (a scientist who studies earthquakes) named Andrija Mohorovičić (1857–1936). It is called the Mohorovičić Discontinuity after him, or Moho for short. The rock beneath the Moho is denser and more elastic than the crustal rock above it.

The Mantle

The region of Earth that lies below the Moho is called the mantle. It is about 1,793 miles (2,885 km) thick.

The mantle is made up of several layers. The uppermost part is solid. The upper mantle

THE DOLOMITES
(opposite) **in northeastern Italy are part of the Alps, which in turn are part of the Alpine-Himalayan chain of mountains that extend from western Europe to eastern Asia. The Dolomites are composed of sedimentary rocks. About 65 million years ago these jagged peaks formed the bed of a sea.**

and the crust together form the lithosphere. Below the lithosphere is the asthenosphere. This layer extends from about 47 to 155 miles (75 to 250 km) below the surface, and lies above a layer of solid rock, down to about 217 to 230 miles (350 to 370 km). Up to 10 percent of the rocks in the asthenosphere are molten.

Molten rock of the upper mantle mixed with molten rock from the base of the crust is called magma. When it reaches the surface through volcanoes, it solidifies as lava. Below that there is a transition zone in which the density increases, leading to the lower mantle. This extends about 1,389 miles (2,235 km) to the boundary of the Earth's core.

The Gutenberg Discontinuity

Beneath the lower mantle, and about 1,815 miles (2,920 km) below our feet, there is another boundary. Discovered by a German seismologist, Beno Gutenberg (1889–1960), this is called the Gutenberg Discontinuity, and it marks the boundary between the solid rock of the mantle and the liquid of the Earth's outer core.

The Core

The outer core is made not from rock but from iron mixed with about 10 to 15 percent by weight of sulfur. It is liquid and about 1,140 miles (1,835 km) thick.

Within the outer core lies the inner core, which is solid and made from almost pure iron. It is a sphere with a radius of about 1,025 miles (1,650 km), and its temperature is about 10,800°F (6,000°C).

THE BROKEN CRUST

The rocks of the crust are solid, but the crust itself is thin. Although it forms a continuous cover over the Earth—there are no gaps where the mantle is exposed—the cover is made up of many pieces, made from lithosphere (the crust plus the upper mantle) and called lithospheric plates. Some of these plates move in relation to each other.

How Plates Move

People noticed long ago, while studying a map of the world, that the continent of Africa looked as though it might once have fitted into the Caribbean and against South America. South

PRINCIPAL MOUNTAINS OF EACH CONTINENT

Continent	Height * feet	meters	Country/Region
AFRICA			
Kilimanjaro	19,340	5,895	Tanzania
Kenya	17,057	5,199	Kenya
Ruwenzori	16,762	5,109	Uganda/Dem. Rep. of the Congo
ASIA			
Everest	29,028	8,848	Nepal/Tibet
K2 (Godwin Austen)	28,251	8,611	Nepal/Kashmir
Kanchenjunga	28,208	8,598	Nepal/India
EUROPE			
Mont Blanc	15,771	4,807	France/Italy
Monte Rosa	15,203	4,634	Italy/Switzerland
Dom	14,911	4,545	Switzerland
NORTH AMERICA			
McKinley	20,321	6,194	USA (Alaska)
Logan	19,849	6,050	Canada
Citlaltepetl	18,701	5,700	Mexico
SOUTH AMERICA			
Aconcagua	22,834	6,960	Argentina
Bonete	22,546	6,872	Argentina
Ojos del Salado	22,516	6,863	Argentina/Chile
OCEANIA			
Puncak Jaya	16,499	5,029	Indonesia
Puncak Mandala	15,617	4,760	Indonesia
Puncak Trikora	15,584	4,750	Indonesia

*above sea level
(The ten highest mountains in the world are all in Asia, either in the Himalayas or in the Karakorum mountain range.)

African and Australian scientists also discovered that their widely separated lands both experienced ice ages at the same time. Plants have been found that grow in places separated by vast oceans. Southern beeches (*Nothofagus*), for example, occur naturally in Australasia and Chile—and nowhere else. The rocks of Northern Ireland and northwestern Scotland match those of eastern Canada.

A large body of evidence began to indicate that the continents have not always occupied their present positions. It was tempting to suppose that the simplest explanation for the distribution of plants, ice ages, and rocks was that continents had formerly been joined. Yet scientists had great difficulty accepting the idea. They could not imagine how continents might move. Then, from the 1940s onward, studies of the ocean floor began to provide further information about the Earth.

It was learned that continental and oceanic crust are different, in age as well as thickness. Nowhere is the oceanic crust more than 160 million years old, but some rocks found in the continental crust are about 4,000 million years old. Then it was discovered that the rocks that lie on either side of a mid-ocean ridge are youngest at the ridge, and that their age increases with increasing distance. Many regions of earthquake and volcanic activity were found to occur along clearly defined lines.

Finally, a mechanism was discovered, a natural process that could make plates move. Convection currents are produced in the mantle when material, heated at great depth, expands and drifts very slowly upward. These currents generate forces that push sections of lithosphere, making them move. Although the mantle is solid, the forces are sufficient to carry the lighter lithospheric rocks across its surface. It is because of these forces that the lithosphere forms plates rather than a single, continuous covering.

Once plates are in motion, the weight of rock at ridges pushes apart the plates to either side, and the leading edge of a sinking plate pulls the rest of the plate behind it.

In 1967 Dan McKenzie of the University of Cambridge, England, brought together all the discoveries of recent years to produce an explanation most scientists quickly accepted. It is called the theory of plate tectonics. (To scientists, a theory is an explanation that can be tested, not just a guess.) Geologists use the word "tectonic" to describe those movements of the Earth's crust that deform rocks.

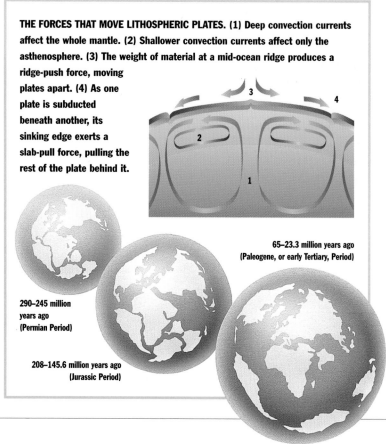

THE FORCES THAT MOVE LITHOSPHERIC PLATES. (1) Deep convection currents affect the whole mantle. (2) Shallower convection currents affect only the asthenosphere. (3) The weight of material at a mid-ocean ridge produces a ridge-push force, moving plates apart. (4) As one plate is subducted beneath another, its sinking edge exerts a slab-pull force, pulling the rest of the plate behind it.

65–23.3 million years ago (Paleogene, or early Tertiary, Period)

290–245 million years ago (Permian Period)

208–145.6 million years ago (Jurassic Period)

THE SAN ANDREAS FAULT
in California lies along a
"conservative" margin:
the Pacific Plate is
moving north, past the
North American Plate,
which is moving in the
opposite direction. The
motion is jerky and
causes earthquakes.

**THE DRIFT OF THE
CONTINENTS** over the
last 300 million years
(left). The continents
were originally grouped
together as one super-
continent, Pangaea. This
gradually fragmented to
form the continents we
know today.

Retracing the Movements of the Continents

Once scientists accepted that the continents had moved, they began calculating where they had been positioned at various times in the past. About 500 million years ago the continents had been dispersed around the world, but not in the positions they occupy today. Little by little, forces in the mantle pushed them toward each other, and by about 300 million years ago they had united to form a single "supercontinent." This is called Pangaea (from the Greek *pan*, meaning "all," and *gaea* or *gaia* meaning "Earth"). Pangaea was surrounded by a vast ocean called Panthalassa (*thalassa* means "sea" in Greek).

The mantle forces continued, and around 300 million years ago Pangaea started to break apart. It formed two large continents, Laurasia and Gondwana. Laurasia comprised all of what are now the continents of the Northern Hemisphere, and Gondwana comprised the southern continents. Laurasia and Gondwana were separated by a sea called Tethys—which is the name of a daughter of Uranus (Heaven) and Gaia (Earth) in Greek mythology.

Starting about 170 million years ago, Laurasia and Gondwana split into the continents we know today. Parts of Laurasia and Gondwana have approached each other, closing up the Tethys Sea. The Mediterranean Sea is all that now remains of Tethys. The continents are still drifting.

North and South America each ride on their own plates. These do not end at the coast, but extend to the middle of the Atlantic Ocean, where they lie next to the African Plate in the south and the Eurasian Plate in the north.

Together with the Pacific, Antarctic, and Indian (or Indo-Australian) Plates these are known as major plates.

Most of the Pacific Ocean lies on the Pacific Plate, but some of the eastern part, from Central America to southern Chile, is on the Nazca Plate, and a smaller portion north of that on the Cocos Plate. These are called minor plates. Other minor plates include the Caribbean, Arabian, and Philippine Plates.

There are also microplates, which are still smaller; these include the Gorda Plate to the west of Oregon, the Juan de Fuca Plate in the eastern North Pacific, from California to British Columbia, and the Hellenic Plate in the eastern Mediterranean.

Plate Margins

Mid-ocean ridges occur at the boundary, or margin, between two plates that are moving apart. Magma rising from the mantle erupts between the plates and solidifies at the surface. It exerts a "ridge-push" force, pushing the plates apart. Because new rock is being formed at these margins, they are called constructive or accretionary. Down the center of the Atlantic Ocean there is an irregular but continuous ridge, where erupting magma has formed a line of submarine mountains and volcanoes. There are similar mid-ocean ridges in the Indian Ocean, where the Pacific and Southern Oceans meet, and elsewhere.

In other places plates are moving together. Where this occurs, and if one set of rocks is much denser than the other, one plate tends to sink below the other—it is said to be subducted, which literally means "brought under." As the subducting plate sinks, it exerts a "slab-pull" force that drags the rest of the plate behind it.

When this happens, it creates a "destructive" margin, and often it produces a deep trench in the ocean floor. The Peru–Chile Trench lies along the destructive margin between the South American and Nazca Plates, for example; the Tonga Trench between the Pacific and Indian Plates; and the Japan Trench between the Pacific and Eurasian Plates. The deepest point on the surface of the Earth is at the bottom of the Mariana Trench, between the Pacific and Philippine Plates. It is 6.8 miles (11 km) deep.

If plates collide when rocks are of a similar density (for example, where two masses of continental crust meet), neither will sink. The two ram into each other, thickening and often crumpling the crust.

At other margins plates are moving past each other in opposite directions. These are called "conservative" margins because material is neither gained nor lost at these margins. The line between them is said to be marked by transform faults.

"Passive" and "Active" Plate Margins

Not all plates move. Some ceased to move long ago, and their margins are now "passive." Certain types of rock are formed when plates collide, and separating plates produce lines of volcanoes. The existence of these rocks and extinct volcanoes sometimes allows geologists to identify where old plate margins that are now sealed and quiet once were.

"Active" margins, where movement is still taking place, can be areas of violence. When plates move, they seldom do so smoothly.

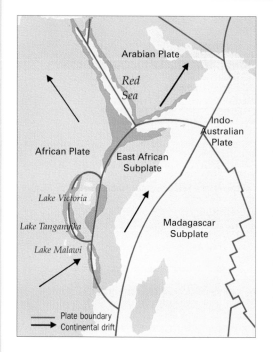

THE RIFT VALLEY *(left)* in East Africa lies along the margins of several plates that are linked to part of a ridge that is opening up the Red Sea. If the present plate movements continue, millions of years from now the East African subplate may eventually split from the mainland; East Africa would then be an island, and the Rift Valley would be a narrow strait.

FORMATION OF THE RIFT VALLEY *(below).* Millions of years ago the upward movement of material beneath the Earth's crust caused gigantic faulting of the rocks in the area, forming the Rift Valley.

As the plates move apart, a deep rift is formed between them. Magma flows to the surface and cools to become the new valley floor. The plates continue to move, carrying the rift structures with them.

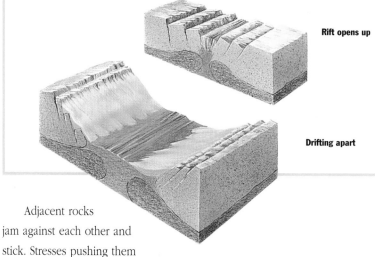

Rift opens up

Drifting apart

Adjacent rocks jam against each other and stick. Stresses pushing them accumulate until suddenly the resistance is overcome and there are one or more jerky movements. These cause earthquakes. Active plate margins are also volcanically active.

WHEN CONTINENTS SPLIT

As plates move apart, the rocks on both sides of the break fracture and sink down—geologists call this faulting. Faults are named according to the way the rocks move. If a section of rock moves

downward at an angle of more than 50° to the horizontal, the fault is "normal." In a "reverse" fault the rock is displaced upward. If one block of rock moves horizontally in relation to the other, the result is a "strike-slip," or "tear," fault.

Between plates the faulted rocks may form a deep depression called a graben (from the

OLDUVAI GORGE, in Tanzania, forms part of the Rift Valley. Fossils of some of the earliest human ancestors have been found there. The gorge is 295 feet (90 m) deep.

German word for "trench"). Rocks thrust upward in this way produce a ridge of land called a horst (from the German word for "bank"). The graben runs the entire length of the constructive margin as a rift. Usually, it happens beneath the ocean, but it can also happen on land when continental plates separate. The clearest example of this is the Rift Valley in East Africa.

Africa started to break apart 25 to 35 million years ago as the African Plate began moving northwest and the East African Subplate moved north. The Rift Valley now extends from Turkey, along the Red Sea, through Ethiopia and Kenya, and into the Indian Ocean at the mouth of the Zambezi River, a total distance of about 6,200 miles (10,000 km). The rift is still active. Faulting sometimes occurs on the floor of the graben, and there are occasional volcanic eruptions.

The Red Sea

About 15 million years ago the Arabian Plate began to move along the line of the Carlsberg Ridge separating the Arabian and Indo-Australian Plates. Arabia started moving away from Africa, opening a section of the Rift Valley that immediately flooded with water from the Arabian Sea. This flooded valley is now the Red Sea, about 1,400 miles (2,250 km) long, 220 miles (355 km) across at its widest point, and in places 9,975 feet (3,040 m) deep.

Arabia and Africa are still moving apart, and the Red Sea is growing wider. Eventually, it may become a vast ocean. At present it is an early stage of a cycle first suggested by a Canadian geophysicist, John Tuzo Wilson (1908–1993). The cycle begins with plate movements that produce rift valleys. Then the valley floors sink further,

FOLDS AND FAULTS. These form when sedimentary rocks are subjected to horizontal or vertical pressure. The rocks will bend until the pressure becomes too great; at this point they shear, forming a fault.

TYPES OF FAULT

Reverse (due to compression)

Raised block (horst)

Rift valley (graben)

Normal

Strike-slip (tear)

TYPES OF FOLD

Anticline

Overfold (overturned)

Syncline

Recumbent

Nappe (thrust fault)

MAKING MOUNTAINS *(right).* When two continental plates separated by a shallow sea collide, one is forced beneath the other. The trapped sediments are folded and pushed up to form mountain ranges. When crust is forced down into the mantle as one

the sides continue to separate, and the valley is flooded to form a narrow sea with parallel sides. This is the stage the Red Sea has reached.

If the process continues, the narrow sea will widen until it becomes an ocean, with a mid-ocean ridge from which its floor continues to spread. It then resembles the Atlantic Ocean, with oceanic crust forming between continents.

Eventually, this becomes unstable, and one of the plates starts sinking into the asthenosphere, producing a trench and an

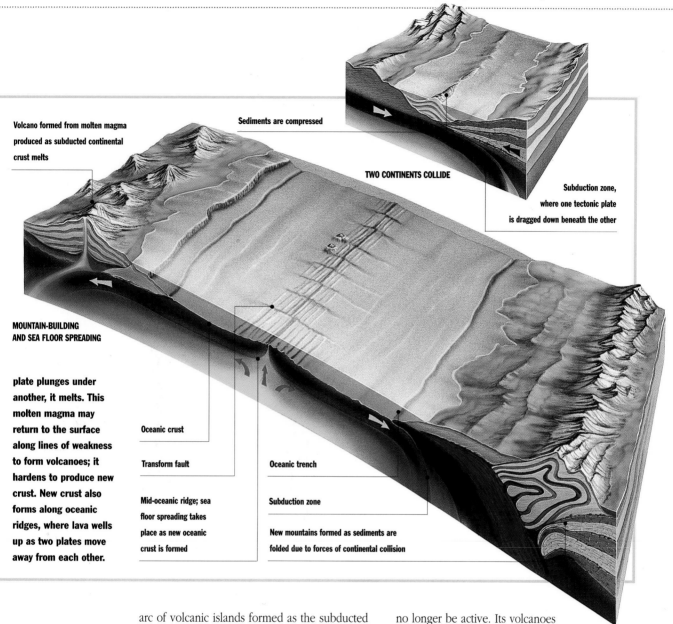

Volcano formed from molten magma produced as subducted continental crust melts

Sediments are compressed

TWO CONTINENTS COLLIDE

Subduction zone, where one tectonic plate is dragged down beneath the other

MOUNTAIN-BUILDING AND SEA FLOOR SPREADING

plate plunges under another, it melts. This molten magma may return to the surface along lines of weakness to form volcanoes; it hardens to produce new crust. New crust also forms along oceanic ridges, where lava wells up as two plates move away from each other.

Oceanic crust

Transform fault

Mid-oceanic ridge; sea floor spreading takes place as new oceanic crust is formed

Oceanic trench

Subduction zone

New mountains formed as sediments are folded due to forces of continental collision

arc of volcanic islands formed as the subducted rock melts, mixes with mantle material to form magma, and erupts through volcanoes big enough to rise above the ocean's surface. The Pacific Ocean has reached this stage. It is shrinking, and will continue to do so until all the oceanic crust between continents has been subducted. The Mediterranean is at a late stage of this part of the cycle. Finally, the sea will disappear, and the continents will collide. The plate margin will be sealed, and eventually it will

no longer be active. Its volcanoes will be stilled, and there will be no more earthquakes.

WHEN CONTINENTS COLLIDE

Part of the Tethys Sea once lay between India and the Asian mainland. India was an island, but an island that was being carried northward on the Indo-Australian Plate. Gradually, the sea grew smaller, and about 40 million years ago it disappeared entirely as the "island" of India rammed into the continent of Asia.

At first oceanic crust on the Indo-Australian Plate was subducted beneath the continental crust of the Eurasian Plate. Volcanoes and mountains formed, just as they have done in western America. When the land of India reached the land of Asia, however, the situation changed. Now continental crust was being pushed hard against continental crust. Neither could be subducted, because both were of similar density.

As they were forced together, the crust thickened and crumpled—like a tablecloth that is pushed from either side. The surface was raised higher and higher, the northern part as the Tibetan Plateau, the southern part as the Himalayas. Although the continental collision began about 40 million years ago, most of the mountain formation occurred less than 20 million years ago. The crust beneath the plateau is now 50 miles (80 km) thick, and India has not ceased its northward movement. The Himalayas may still be rising, but very slowly.

The Alps in Europe were formed in the same way, in this case by the collision between the African and Eurasian Plates. This collision has not yet closed the Mediterranean—the remnant of the Tethys still separates the two continents.

THE FORMATION OF MOUNTAIN RANGES

Constructive margins do not produce mountain ranges, but destructive ones do. As a plate made from oceanic crust is dragged below a lighter,

more buoyant, continental plate, its rocks enter the hot asthenosphere, where they melt.

It is not a smooth, gentle process. The rocks fracture, and the cracks fill with sediments and water; these are also carried into the asthenosphere. The subducting rock fractures the overlying rock, the water vaporizes and expands, and volcanoes form on the ocean floor behind the region where lithospheric rock is being subducted—the subduction zone.

Magma also moves upward through cracks beneath the continental crust, forming volcanoes on the landward side. Sedimentary rocks that have formed above the hard, igneous rock of the oceanic crust are pressed against the edge of the continental crust. These pile up as a jumbled mix

ANNAPURNA, in the Himalayas, is one of the world's highest mountains, rising to 26,504 feet (8,078 m) above sea level. The mountains result from the crumpling of the crust as India collided with Asia.

COLLISION BETWEEN CONTINENTS. About 40 million years ago the Indo-Australian and Eurasian Plates collided. At the start of the collision *(below right)* oceanic crust subducted beneath continental crust, and sedimentary rocks and volcanoes formed mountains in Asia. Now *(below left)*, the sea basin has closed, and continental crust is pushing into continental crust. The map *(right)* shows the northward movement of the Indo-Australian Plate and the collision between it and the Eurasian Plate.

EURASIAN PLATE

As the plates converge, the ocean disappears; the Indian Plate collides with the Eurasian Plate, and ocean sediments and parts of the oceanic crust are thrust upward to form the new mountain chain

40 MILLION YEARS AGO

Mountains are formed by volcanic activity at plate margin

Oceanic crust forced beneath Eurasian Plate

Sediments

Ripple effect of collision forms mountains and Plateau of Tibet

PRESENT

Indian plate moves north

Collision features
Zone of compression
Igneous rocks mixed with ocean sediments
Thrust fault
Strike-slip fault

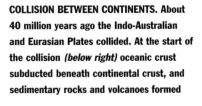

of rocks called a melange (from the French *mêler*, "to mix"). This can be raised to a considerable height.

The World's Longest Mountain Chain

Both American plates are moving westward. This is carrying the South American Plate against the Nazca Plate. The oceanic crust, being denser, is sinking below the continental crust. The collision is breaking the continental rocks into a series of grabens and horsts. Cracks right through the crust allow magma to rise, producing many volcanoes. The Andes are the result of this collision. The Rocky Mountains result from the subduction of the Pacific Plate beneath the North American Plate. In both cases the descending plates are at an angle of 45° to 60°.

During the past 20 million years parts of the Andes have grown more than 5,000 feet (1,500 m) in height. The collision between the Nazca and South American Plates was fairly recent—as measured by the timescale geologists use—although less recent than that between India and Asia. It began during the latter part of the Cretaceous Period, less than about 100 million years ago, and not quite 10 million years have passed since Panama collided with Colombia.

Many of the rocks found in the Andes are sedimentary, and some contain fossils of marine animals. These show that rocks now forming high mountains once lay at or below sea level, and they are not the only signs of this occurrence. There are rock formations that clearly were once shorelines, and in many places throughout the range there are surfaces that could only have formed close to sea level.

The Andes are the longest mountain chain in the world, lying parallel to the Pacific coast of South America and extending from the Caribbean coast of Venezuela to Tierra del Fuego in southern Chile. The width of the range averages 150 miles (240 km), but it is much wider at about latitude 18°S, in Bolivia, than elsewhere. In Colombia and Venezuela the range divides into the western, central, and eastern cordilleras.

THE FORMATION OF THE ANDES as the South American Plate moves westward against the Nazca Plate. The Peru–Chile Trench is in the bend where the subducting Nazca Plate descends below the South American Plate.

EARTHQUAKES

Earthquakes are common, providing clear evidence of continuing movement along the plate margins. An earthquake is a shaking of the

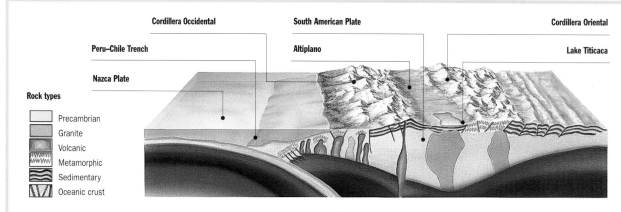

Cordillera Occidental

South American Plate

Cordillera Oriental

Peru–Chile Trench

Altiplano

Lake Titicaca

Nazca Plate

Rock types

Precambrian
Granite
Volcanic
Metamorphic
Sedimentary
Oceanic crust

ground caused by the sudden movement of rocks. Where two masses of rock are being pushed in different directions, friction binds them together. The strain accumulates until it overcomes the friction and the rocks move. The strain is released, usually in a series of jerks. The place where this happens is called the focus, or hypocenter, of the earthquake. The place on the surface above the focus is called the epicenter.

Earthquakes occur at varying depths. They are described as shallow if their focus is less than 43.5 miles (70 km) below the surface, intermediate if they occur 43.5–186 miles (70–299 km) below ground, and deep if their focus is below 186 miles (299 km). No earthquakes occur below 447 miles (719 km).

Seismic Waves and Earthquake Magnitude

The shock of the earthquake is transmitted through the rocks as "seismic" waves. There are two types of seismic waves, called P and S. P stands for primary or pressure, and S for

THE ANDES include some of the world's highest mountains. This scene is in the Altiplano in the Cordillera Oriental, the eastern range in southern Peru.

secondary or shear. The waves travel through the Earth. P waves can travel through gases, liquids, and solids, but S waves travel only through solids, and the denser the rocks, the faster seismic waves move.

When studying earthquakes, seismologists use instruments called seismometers that can detect P and S waves. The readings are printed as lines on a seismograph that show the amount of vertical movement of the surface at five-second intervals. From the order in which different waves arrive, and by comparing readings from instruments in many different locations, seismologists can find the focus and epicenter of an earthquake and can calculate its magnitude from the intensity of the waves.

The magnitude of an earthquake is usually reported as a value on the Richter scale, which was devised by the American physicist Charles Francis Richter (1900–1985). It always refers to the magnitude at the epicenter. A difference of 1 on the Richter scale represents a difference of 10 in the extent to which surface rocks move and a difference of 30 in the amount of energy the earthquake releases.

An earthquake with a magnitude of more than about 5.0 on the Richter scale may cause damage to buildings—but magnitude is a poor indication of the injuries people may suffer. This depends on the number of people in the area and the type of buildings around them. In 1994 an earthquake of magnitude 8.2 in the Kuril Islands killed all the people there at the time—16 Russian soldiers. In 1995 an earthquake of a smaller magnitude, 7.2, struck the city of Kobe, Japan, but because it occurred in a densely populated area, 6,000 people died.

FAULTS AND EARTHQUAKES. At the focus of an earthquake stress energy is suddenly released when blocks of rock, deformed when portions of the Earth's crust converge or slide past each other, move to a new position. The shock waves trigger landslides on steep slopes and cause water-saturated sediments to liquefy. One block of rock can move several yards or meters in relation to its neighbor, wreaking havoc that may include flooding. In a "normal" fault stretching rocks break vertically along a steep fault plane. A strike-slip, or tear, fault involves horizontal shearing along a vertical plane.

FAULTS

Strike-slip fault

Normal fault

IMPACT OF AN EARTHQUAKE

Two adjoining plates move laterally along the fault line

Epicenter

Landslides may take place on hilly ground

Shock waves

Focus

Earth movements cause flooding in low-lying areas

Liquefaction of recent sediments causes buildings to sink

A LANDSLIDE at the village of Otaki in the mountains of Hokkaido, Japan, caused by an earthquake. The hillside has collapsed, shearing away the road and destroying a house.

MAJOR EARTHQUAKES SINCE 1990

Year	Location	Magnitude (Richter scale)	Deaths
1998	Afghanistan	6.1	5,000
1997	N.E. Iran	7.1; 5.5	1,500
	E. Venezuela	6.9	79
	Xinjiang Uygur, China	6.4; 6.3	12
	N.E. Iran	5.4; 6.1; 5.7	72
	N.W. Iran	6.1; 5.2	995
	India	6.1	30
	Sulawesi, Indonesia	6.0	17
1996	Biak Island, Indonesia	7.9	108
	Lijiang, China	7.0	240
	Xinjiang Uygur, China	6.9; 5.1	28
	Nazca, Peru	6.4	not known
	Ecuador	5.9	19
	Bautou, Mongolia	5.9	18
1995	Mexico	7.6	65
	Sakhalin Island, Russia	7.5	1,990
	Kobe, Japan	7.2	6,000
	Sumatra, Indonesia	7.0	100
	Yunnan Province, China	6.5	40
	Pereira, Colombia	6.4	38
	Egion, Greece	6.1	17
	Turkey	6.0	84
1994	Kuril Islands	8.2	16
	Sumatra, Indonesia	7.2	215
	Los Angeles, USA	6.8	61
	Halmahera, Indonesia	6.8	7
	N. Algeria	5.6	171
1993	N. Japan	7.8	185
	Maharashtra State, India	6.4	9,700
1992	Erzincan, Turkey	6.8	500
	Cairo, Egypt	5.9	550
	Pakistan	5.5	36
1991	Costa Rica and Panama	7.4	82
	Georgia, USSR	7.1	114
	Pakistan and Afghanistan	6.8	1,200
	N. Iraq	5.6	20
	Guatemala	5.8	17
1990	Iran	7.7	40,000
	Philippines	7.7	1,600
	Qinghai Province, China	6.9	109
	Romania	6.9	10

[Note: In addition to these there were other earthquakes, the magnitudes of which were not reported. These have not been included.]

MOUNTAINS THAT EXPLODE

A volcano is an opening at the surface of the Earth through which magma sometimes flows. Magma is hot, molten rock from the mantle. When it cools and solidifies, it is called lava. Volcanoes are not necessarily shaped like mountains. Magma can seep gently to the surface and spread widely, solidifying as a horizontal sheet. Lava solidified as basalt rock covers about

772,000 square miles (2 million sq. km) in South Africa to a depth of almost 2,300 feet (700 m). Volcanoes can also disappear. Below the grasslands in parts of southern Peru the rocks are beds of lava up to 1.5 miles (2.4 km) thick. This was erupted long ago from volcanoes in the Andes. Some ancient volcanoes along this chain no longer erupt and have been eroded so much that little of them remains. Others are still active.

The height and shape of a volcano depend on the material from which it is made. Lavas are not all of the same composition, and volcanoes eject rocks, ash, and gases as well as molten rock. The highest volcanoes are made from alternating layers of lava and rock debris, called pyroclastics. These rocks were thrown high into the air, some molten and others as hot but solidified fragments. A volcano of this type is called a composite volcano, or strato-volcano. Mount Fuji, in Japan, and Mount Vesuvius, in Italy, are typical of composite volcanoes.

"Shield" volcanoes are not usually so tall and have sides that slope more gently. They are made from very runny lava that flows a long way before it hardens. Mauna Kea and Mauna Loa, in Hawaii, are shield volcanoes. Both are more than 13,000 feet (4,000 m) high.

Pyroclastic cones, also called ash and cinder, or scoria, cones, are made by very thick lava that breaks into fragments of rock mixed with ash and cinders. They are often small, with very steep sides, but not always. Paricutín, in Mexico, is a volcano of this type that is about 1,000 feet (300 m) high.

Lava may also form a dome. A lava dome volcano can reach a considerable size. One of the largest is Lassen Peak, in California. Its base has a diameter of about 2 miles (3.2 km), and it is more than 2,000 feet (600 m) tall.

Famous Eruptions

On August 24, A.D. 79, Gaius Plinius Secundus, better known as Pliny the Elder, was a government official in charge of the Roman fleet at Misenium, on the northern side of the Bay of Naples, when he saw Mount Vesuvius begin to erupt across the bay. Pliny sailed to the southern shore to try to help those in danger, but he was overcome by ash and gases from the eruption and died. The cities of Herculaneum and Pompeii were overwhelmed, burying Pompeii beneath 20 feet (6 m) of ash and Herculaneum beneath a similar thickness of mud.

It was a very explosive eruption. A rising mixture of gases and hot magma mixed with air, heating it so that the air expanded rapidly. This made the material rise even faster, so it was thrown into the air as a huge column. This type of eruption is called plinian, in memory of Pliny.

About 2,000 people died in that eruption. The biggest eruption of modern times was also of the plinian type. It happened in April 1815 on

VOLCANIC ERUPTIONS SINCE 1990

	Number killed
1990, Mt. Kelud, E. Java, Indonesia	17
1991, Mt. Unzen, Japan	38
Mt. Pinatubo, Philippines	800
1993, Galeras, Colombia	9
Mayon, Philippines	68
1994, Mt. Merapi, Java, Indonesia	31
1996, Manam Island, Papua New Guinea	12
1997, Soufrière Hills and Chances Peak, Montserrat	19

CROSS-SECTION THROUGH MOUNT ETNA, SICILY. Mount Etna is always active. The peak is at a height of more than 10,000 feet (3,000 m), and its base covers an area of about 500 square miles (1,295 sq. km), making it the highest volcano in Europe and the biggest mountain in Italy south of the Alps. Its name in Greek is *Aitne*, from *aitho*, which means "I burn."

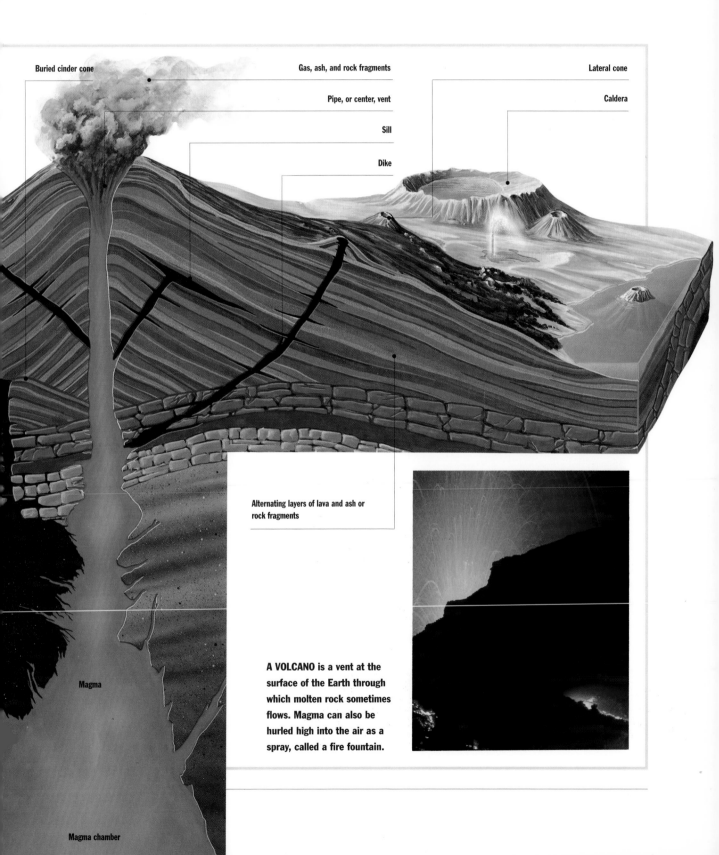

Buried cinder cone

Gas, ash, and rock fragments

Lateral cone

Pipe, or center, vent

Caldera

Sill

Dike

Alternating layers of lava and ash or rock fragments

Magma

Magma chamber

A VOLCANO is a vent at the surface of the Earth through which molten rock sometimes flows. Magma can also be hurled high into the air as a spray, called a fire fountain.

MOUNT ST. HELENS *(opposite)*, a composite volcano in the Cascade Range, Washington State, soon after it erupted on May 18, 1980. The explosion triggered many snowfalls and removed the entire north face of the mountain in a major avalanche. This avalanche was overtaken by an air blast carrying hot ash and rock fragments, followed finally by a flow of burning pumice and ash. A second, smaller eruption occurred on May 25.

the island of Sumbawa, in what is now Indonesia, when Mount Tambora exploded. About 12 cubic miles (50 cu. km) of rock, dust, and ash was hurled into the air, reducing the height of the volcano from 13,450 feet (4,100 m) to its present height of 9,255 feet (2,820 m), and leaving a crater up to 4.5 miles (7 km) in diameter and 3,300 feet (1,000 m) deep. Ash fell over a radius of 620 miles (1,000 km). Crops and livestock were destroyed too, causing up to 50,000 deaths from hunger in addition to those killed by the eruption. About 35,000 people had to leave the island. Fine ash from this eruption rose to such a great height that it was carried around the world and shaded the surface; 1816 was known as the year with no summer.

Krakatau, on a tiny island in the Sunda Strait between Java and Sumatra, erupted in 1883. It had not erupted since 1680, and that eruption was fairly minor. This time rumblings began in

May, with clouds of ash and steam and explosions that could be heard over a long distance. At about 1 P.M. on August 26 there was the first of a series of much bigger explosions; an hour later a cloud of black ash rose to a height of about 19 miles (30 km). The following morning, just after 10 A.M., the side of the volcano collapsed, the sea rushed in and met the hot magma, and the entire volcano vanished in an explosion that was heard on Rodriguez Island, almost 3,000 miles (4,800 km) away.

Krakatau had fallen into its empty "magma chamber" (see page 26) below sea level. This caused a series of "tsunamis"—waves that travel fast and can cause severe damage. One of these was about 120 feet (37 m) high when it reached the shores of Java and Sumatra, killing 36,000 people. The explosion threw about 5 cubic miles (20 cu. km) of ash into the air, some of it to a height of 50 miles (80 km). It was three years before the last of it fell to the ground.

Mount Pelée, in Martinique, erupted on May 8, 1902. This was a "peléean" eruption, named after the mountain. Eruptions of this type produce an avalanche of magma fragments and burning gases beneath a cloud of hot ash—sometimes called a *nuée ardente* (French for "blazing cloud")—that moves at up to 100 mph (160 km/h), killing every plant and animal in its path. The eruption destroyed the city of St. Pierre, killing 30,000 people. The only survivor was a prisoner in the jail, confined in a windowless cell.

How Volcanoes Work

Although no two volcanoes are quite the same, they all share similar basic features. Below

MAIN TYPES OF VOLCANIC CONE. Not all volcanoes are steep-sided, conical mountains with a crater at the top. Their shape varies considerably, depending on how runny the lava was when it erupted and how much ash and rock was mixed with it.

Pyroclastic

Lava dome

Composite

Lava shield

ground magma is rising under pressure through weaknesses in the rocks—most commonly at a plate margin. The heat of the magma melts some of the rock above. Different rocks melt at different temperatures, and rocks with low melting temperatures become part of the magma. There is now a mass of molten rock surrounded by solid rock. This is called a magma chamber. The molten rock inside it is held there because the melting temperature of the surrounding rock is higher than the temperature of the magma.

The contents of the magma chamber are under pressure from the magma rising from below, but above the magma chamber there is another line of weakness. This leads almost to the surface. It is called a chimney.

Eventually, the pressure in the magma chamber is so great that it blasts away rock that is partly sealing the chimney. Magma rises up the chimney, and there is an eruption. The eruption empties the magma chamber below ground, but a large mass of lava accumulates above ground. The weight of the lava causes the structure to collapse into the magma chamber, leaving a crater, often called a caldera.

Together, the magma chamber, chimney, and crater are the essential components of every volcano. There may be more than one magma chamber and more than one chimney. With the shield volcanoes of Hawaii, for example, there is a primary magma chamber about 37 miles (60 km) below sea level that feeds a secondary magma chamber, a few hundred yards (meters) across, just below the volcano. An eruption empties the secondary magma chamber, but leaves the rocks weakened so it fills again from the primary chamber.

Types of Eruption

There are several types of volcanic eruption in addition to the plinian and peléean described above. The differences depend partly on the composition of the magma.

Magma contains varying amounts of silica (silicon dioxide, SiO_2, from which quartz is made). The more silica it contains, the more viscous—stickier—it is when it erupts and becomes lava. Hawaiian magma contains very little silica so it is very runny. It flows a long way, and eruptions are accompanied by huge, continuous sprays of magma called fire fountains. Hawaiian-type eruptions usually occur on ocean islands; in Iceland, for example.

Strombolian eruptions, named after Stromboli, the island volcano off the coast of southern Italy, involve magma that is a little more viscous than that of Hawaiian volcanoes. Gases become trapped in pockets within it, producing a series of explosions that throw small rocks and cinders high into the air. Lava often erupts through the flanks of the volcano.

Vulcano is another island volcano in the same group as Stromboli. Its eruptions are extremely violent; vulcanian eruptions are named after it. The magma is fairly viscous, and gases become trapped in it. The pressure from the gases increases until the magma explodes, throwing off the overlying cover of solidified lava. Rocks from the solidified lava, gases, and ash are thrown into the air, but no magma.

Some volcanoes are dormant for long periods then suddenly explode when the pressure of gases inside them reaches a level at which it can blow away the plug of solidified lava sealing the chimney. The eruption is typical

THE KOOLAU MOUNTAINS, on the coast of Oahu, Hawaii, are composed of young, volcanic rocks. Winds from the Pacific Ocean carry moist air; as the air rises, its water vapor condenses, producing heavy rainfall. This has eroded deep gullies in the rocks.

of Vesuvius and is called vesuvian or sub-plinian. It releases very frothy lava that solidifies into pumice, as well as clouds of ash and gases.

When runny lava erupts on the seabed, it solidifies as a rock called pillow lava because of its shape. If the sea is very shallow, however, water flooding into the open vent can cause an extremely violent explosion, with a column of steam, gases, rock fragments, and dust hurled to a height of 12 miles (19 km) or more. In 1963 an eruption of this type just south of Iceland produced a new island called Surtsey, so these eruptions are called Surtseyan.

THE LIFE OF A MOUNTAIN

Mountains are produced by the movement of plates in the crust of the Earth or are erupted onto the surface by volcanoes. No sooner has a mountain been formed than it comes under attack. When rock is heated by the Sun, it expands. As it cools it contracts again. The rock surface, exposed directly to the Sun, is warmed more than the rock beneath, and so it expands more. This can crack the rock. Rocks lower down the mountain will be warmed and will expand more than those higher up.

Near the top of the mountain the temperature may be low enough for snow and ice to lie on the surface for much of the year. This produces a second form of attack. Water seeps into the tiny cracks caused by expansion and contraction. If the water freezes, it expands, widening and lengthening the crack. As pieces fall from the rock surface, a new surface is exposed on which the process is repeated.

MASS WASTING is the loss of material down steep slopes, as rock falls and rock slides. The term "avalanche" is used to cover both types of movement. Pieces of rock released in a rock fall are smashed as they bounce down the gradient. The resulting small stones tend to accumulate as steeply sloping piles of scree. Rock slides carry soil and plants with them.

Rock fall

Rock slide

Mass Wasting

If you walk along the foot of a steep cliff or mountain slope, you may see rocks or stones that have fallen from the cliff or mountainside. This is called scree. Scree is produced by the repeated expansion and contraction of rocks.

Detached rocks fall freely. As they do so, they bound down the side of the slope, crashing into it with great force and dislodging other loose rocks. Large amounts of rock can fall very fast. This is a rock fall.

A rock fall is one way material can be lost down a slope, but there are others. Together they are called mass wasting. Mass wasting on a very large scale constitutes an avalanche.

On more gentle slopes rocks, stones, and soil, sometimes carrying trees and other vegetation, may slide rather than fall freely. This produces a rock slide, or landslide.

Destruction and Renewal

As fragments of rock fall from mountains, they smash against other rocks and break into ever smaller particles. They form soils and sands, and they eventually find their way to the ocean floor. There, as sediments, they are compressed into sedimentary rock, travel with the spreading sea floor, and after millions of years they arrive at a destructive plate margin. They may be subducted back into the asthenosphere, to be melted, remixed, and perhaps thrown skyward again from a volcano. Or they may be pushed upward as a new mountain range.

The Urals were once high mountains. The Himalayas will one day be gone. Mountain ranges become plains, and their rocks are recycled to make new mountains.

A CYCLE OF DESTRUCTION AND RENEWAL. The illustration *(right)* shows the life cycle of a mountain as it might appear in a landscape. The diagram *(below)* shows how the processes involved affect each other. Mountains can be formed from seabed sediments that have been compressed and heated to form sedimentary rocks and then thrust high above the sea by movements of the Earth's crust, or from rock that has risen from below the crust as magma. Rock of this type is called igneous, from the Latin *ignis*, meaning "fire." Eventually, material eroded from the mountain enters the sea; mixed with water, it flows down the slope from the coast and into the deep ocean. This flow is called a turbidity current.

Erosion by rivers

Erosion by wind

Deposition by wind

Erosion by flash floods

Deposition by flash floods

Deposition in lagoons

Deposition by sea currents

Igneous rock — Weathering, transport & deposition — Sediment

Cooling & solidification (crystallization)

Magma

Melting

Heat & pressure (metamorphism)

Weathering, transport & deposition

Weathering, transport & deposition

Cementation & compaction (lithification)

Metamorphic rock — Heat & pressure (metamorphism) — Sedimentary rock

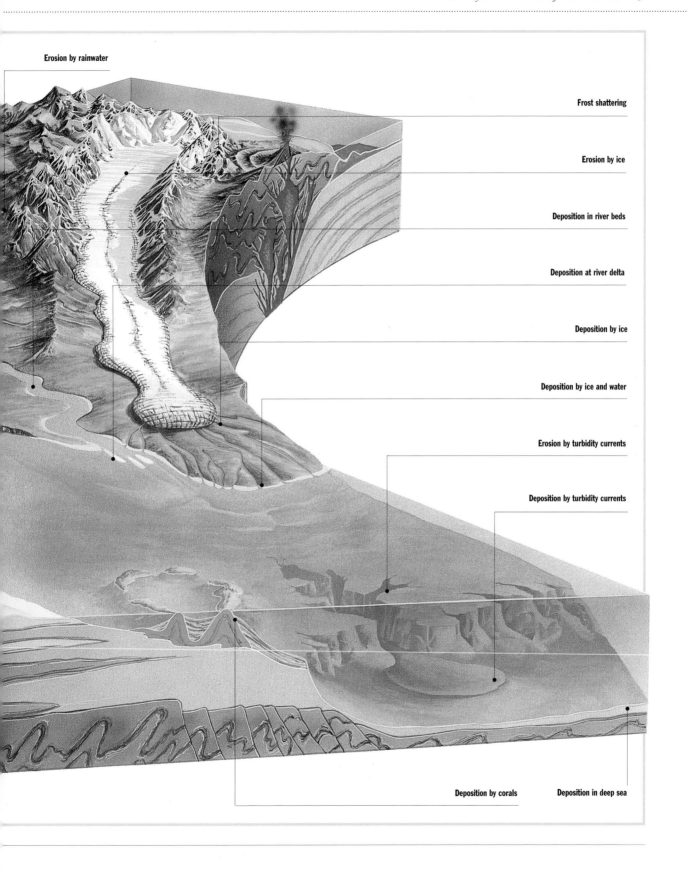

Erosion by rainwater

Frost shattering

Erosion by ice

Deposition in river beds

Deposition at river delta

Deposition by ice

Deposition by ice and water

Erosion by turbidity currents

Deposition by turbidity currents

Deposition by corals

Deposition in deep sea

The Natural World of Mountains

T owering mountains topped with snow create a skyline of breathtaking beauty, but the picture tells only part of the story. Mountains are not simply bare rock. Many plants and animals live on them, yet they are often different from those on the plains at the foot of the mountain range.

MOUNTAIN ENVIRONMENTAL ZONES and the altitudes at which they occur in three tropical regions of the world.

Pictures of the Himalayas show them perpetually capped with snow. So they are, of course, yet they lie approximately between latitudes 26°N and 40°N, in the subtropics. The Andes extend from about 10°N to 50°S, a huge distance, and

they, too, can be cold and bleak—even at the equator.

Mountains in tropical or subtropical regions can be snow-capped because the air temperature decreases with increasing height. Mountaineers climbing in the Himalayas or the central Andes set out in warm temperatures surrounded by lush vegetation. As they climb, the weather becomes steadily colder, and they must put on warmer clothes.

TEMPERATURE AND HEIGHT

Air can be compressed (car tires are filled with compressed air), and it also has weight, so air at a low level is compressed by the weight of the air above it, all the way to the top of the atmosphere. Since compression forces molecules closer together, a given weight of air occupies a smaller volume when it is compressed. This also makes it denser—the same volume of air contains more molecules when the air is compressed than when it is not.

When molecules are close together, they collide more often than when they are far apart. They also gain energy. This additional energy raises the temperature of the air; compressing air therefore makes it warmer.

The opposite is also true. Air pressure decreases with increasing altitude because there is less air pressing down. As the pressure decreases, the density of the air decreases, molecules move farther apart and lose energy, and the air grows cooler. The rate at which the temperature falls is called the lapse rate. This averages 3.5°F per 1,000 feet (6.5°C per km).

Continuous snow	**ANDES OF CENTRAL PERU**		6,000 m (19,700 feet)
	RUWENZORI, EAST AFRICA		5,000 m (16,400 feet)
Alpine zone	Steppe with tree-like Compositae	*Senecio-Lobelia* Scrub and grassland	**EASTERN NEW GUINEA** Alpine grassland Alpine savanna	4,000 m (13,000 feet)
Sub-Alpine	Elfin woodland	Tree heath	High montane forest	3,000 m (9,800 feet)
Montane forest	Mossy forest	Bamboo zone Mossy forest	Mossy forest	2,000 m (6,600 feet)
Transitional submontane forest				1,000 m (3,300 feet)
Tropical rain forest				Sea level

WATERTON LAKES NATIONAL PARK, Alberta, and Glacier National Park, Montana, together make up the world's first international peace park. This was established in 1932 in the Rocky Mountains.

Snow-Capped Peaks

If a mountain is high enough, part of it will be in contact with air that is below freezing temperature. Precipitation will fall as snow; the snow may not melt, even in summer.

Calculating the height at which the air will reach freezing temperature is simple—subtract 32 (freezing temperature) from the temperature in Fahrenheit at sea level, divide the result by 3.5, and the answer is in thousands of feet. Using the Celsius scale, divide the sea-level temperature by 6.5, and the answer is the freezing-level height in

kilometers. If the sea-level temperature is, say, 60°F (15.5°C), the air will be at freezing temperature at 8,000 feet (2,440 m).

This is the height at which there will be permanent snow in parts of the world with a temperate climate. Where climates are colder or warmer, this height will change. In Antarctica, where the sea-level temperature is always below freezing, there is permanent snow on mountains all the way down to sea level. In a hot climate the snow will be much higher, but even at the equator high mountains can retain their caps of

Components of the ecosystem

1 Alpine grasses and heathers
2 Chamois
3 Spanish ibex
4 Snowy vole
5 Brown hare
6 Ptarmigan
7 Golden eagle
8 Lynx
9 Carrion and regurgitated matter
10 Griffon vulture

Energy flow

⟶ Primary producer/ primary consumer

⟶ Primary/secondary consumer

⟶ Dead material/ consumer

snow. If the sea-level temperature is 90°F (32°C), air will be below freezing temperature at about 16,600 feet (5,060 m).

CHANGING VEGETATION

At each level of the mountain, plants that are suited to the temperature and rainfall at that level are found.

In many parts of the tropics you would find rain forest at sea level at the foot of a mountain. Rain forest grows where the rainfall is high and rain falls throughout the year, so there is never a time when the soil dries and plants are short of water.

In higher latitudes the temperature at sea level is lower, and the vegetation is different. In middle latitudes broad-leaved forests, with such trees as oaks and maples, might grow near sea level; in northern regions such as Canada and Scandinavia the forests would be coniferous (composed of trees that bear cones, such as firs and pines). As temperature decreases with height, the vegetation changes, but in high

latitudes the change is less marked because the limit to plant growth is lower.

Farther up the mountain the type of forest changes. You might enter forest where the trees are festooned with mosses and ferns. Such forest is almost always shrouded in mist because it is higher than the base of the clouds. This is called mossy forest, or cloud forest. Above it there is often a region where winds are stronger. Wind dries out the growing tips of trees, stunting their growth. The trees are small and twisted into curious shapes. This is called elfin woodland.

At its upper margin trees in the elfin woodland become increasingly widely spaced. In wet climates there may be scattered, stunted trees beyond the edge of the elfin woodland. This kind of vegetation is called krummholz (from the German for "crooked timber").

Then there are no more trees. Summers are so short that the needles of coniferous trees cannot mature, so the first frost of winter kills them. Spring frosts kill the leaf buds of broad-leaved trees such as beech and ash. Trees cannot grow. This boundary is the tree line or timber line, and because mountain plants were first studied in the European Alps, it is often known by its German name, the baumgrenze.

Above the tree line there are meadows of grasses and wild flowers, with occasional small shrubs. This is the alpine zone of the mountain, where the vegetation resembles that of an alpine meadow. It also resembles the tundra

Primary producers   **Herbivores**   **Carnivores**

A MOUNTAIN ECOSYSTEM showing the relationship between herbivorous and carnivorous creatures. Many of the herbivores spend summer and winter at different altitudes.

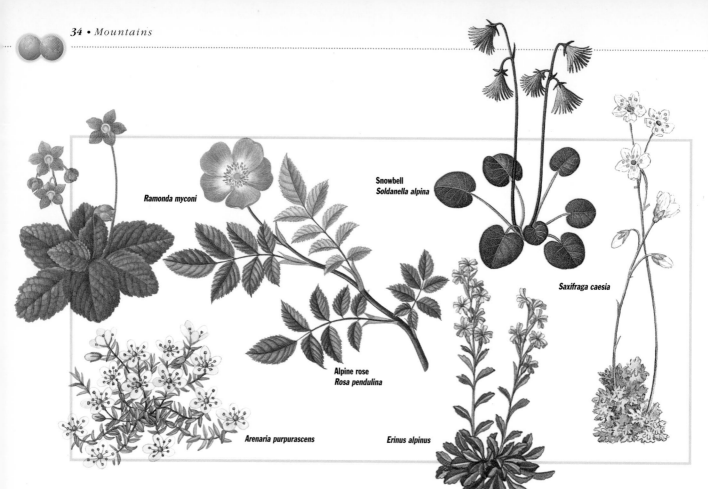

Ramonda myconi

Snowbell
Soldanella alpina

Saxifraga caesia

Alpine rose
Rosa pendulina

Arenaria purpurascens

Erinus alpinus

PLANTS OF THE PYRENEES, the mountain range that lies between France and Spain, are more closely related to plants growing at lower elevations in the same latitude than they are to the plants growing on mountains in the tropics. Pyrenean plants are similar to those found in the European Alps. *Ramonda myconi* grows naturally only in the Pyrenees, although it is grown widely in gardens.

of northern Canada and Siberia, and, like the tundra, it ends where it meets the land of permanent snow.

These divisions are quite general; mountain vegetation varies from one part of the world to another. Many mountains in the Southern Hemisphere are not forested, for example, so they are more extensively covered with grassland. Plants near the equator receive much more intense sunlight than plants in the Arctic, regardless of the air temperature, so grasslands in tropical mountain regions will contain far more species than true tundra.

RAIN AND WIND

Mountains are windy places. On summits in the Rocky Mountains winds in winter blow at an average speed of 27–34 mph (12–15 m/sec.) and often reach 90–112 mph (40–50 m/sec.).

There are two reasons for the strong winds. As moving air crosses a mountain, the air near the surface is forced to rise up one side of the mountain and down the other side. It has to travel farther than the air above it (which continues in a straight line), but it has to arrive at the foot of the mountain at the same time—there cannot be gaps without any air in them! Because it has farther to travel but no more time in which to do so, the air has to move faster. This means the wind at the top of the mountain is stronger than the wind on the plains to either side.

Also, there is less friction higher up. Air traveling close to the ground, or to a lesser extent the sea, is slowed by friction between the air and the surface. On a mountainside more of

THE MOUNT COOK LILY
(Ranunculus lyallii) **is a relative of the buttercup and not a lily. It grows in the Southern Alps of New Zealand. It was once common but now survives only in remote, moist crevices where grazing animals cannot reach it.**

the approaching air is above this level. It starts to move upward, parallel to the mountainside, only when it is quite close, and it is only then that it begins to be slowed by friction.

Whenever air rises, it cools. As air cools, its capacity for holding water vapor decreases. Clouds—masses of water drops or ice crystals—will form in moist air as the air rises to cross a mountain; if the air is moist enough, rain or snow will fall. If it is a high mountain, the air will be fairly dry by the time it reaches the peak. On the other side of the mountain the descending air, which has lost much of its moisture, warms up as it descends; as air grows warmer, its capacity to hold water vapor increases. The air therefore becomes dry; so mountains often have a wetter climate on one side than on the other.

Mountain Winds

Mountains also affect winds in other ways. On fine summer days air near ground level in sheltered valleys becomes very warm. It expands and rises up the sides of the valley as a warm, gentle valley wind. Higher up the sides of the valley it blows a little more strongly. This is because the upper sides are often sunnier than the valley bottom so they are heated more strongly. This is called an anabatic (up-slope) wind. At night the opposite occurs. As the ground cools, cold air from the top of the valley flows downward to collect at the bottom. This is known as a katabatic (down-slope) wind.

As air sinks down the side of a mountain, warming as it does so, a warm, gusty wind can be produced as it reaches the low ground on the far side of the mountain. In North America there is a westerly wind (that is, a wind that originates in the west) of this type that blows on the eastern side of the Rocky Mountains. This is called the chinook. Its effect is most marked in winter, when it can raise the temperature by 60°F (33°C) in less than an hour. In Europe this type of wind is called a föhn wind. Föhn winds are common in winter and spring on the northern side of the Alps, and they also occur in Asia, on the eastern side of the Southern Alps of New Zealand, and, on a smaller scale, in many other parts of the world.

Mountain winds can also be cold, however, if cold, dry air is forced over mountains and—despite warming as it descends the far side—displaces warmer air. This type of wind is called

a bora, and it occurs in a number of places, including Colorado. There, the bora wind can be very strong, with gusts of 100 mph (45 m/sec.) or more.

PLANTS IN A TOUGH CLIMATE

Alpine plants are popular with gardeners for their attractive flowers and their small size, which means a variety of species can be grown in a small area. Herbs that grow in deserts and tundra regions are also small and bright, as they have only a brief time in which to flower and set seed.

Mountain herbs cannot tolerate being shaded by trees, so they grow beyond the tree line. There the summers are cool and short, the winters long and cold, and the growing season—the period during which the weather is warm enough for plants to grow—does not last long.

These plants also have to use water very economically. Rain may fall heavily on one side of a mountain, but the other side is usually dry. Even on the wet side it is not always easy for plants to absorb and retain the water. Soils are thin, and water runs from the surface quickly. The ground is frozen for much of the year, and ice is useless to them: plant roots can absorb water only as a liquid. The climate is also windy, and wind has a powerful drying effect (which is why people hang out laundry to dry in the wind).

Many alpine plants shelter from the wind by

GOAT ANTELOPES live in steep, rocky, remote places throughout the Northern Hemisphere and are famous for their sure-footedness.

Argalis
Ovis ammon

growing close to the ground or in crevices. Some, such as *Arenaria purpurascens*, saxifrages (*Saxifraga* species), and mountain avens (*Dryas octopetala*), grow outward to form mats. These are low enough to be sheltered from the wind by nearby rocks and also cover a wider area of ground than most plants, reducing the rate at which water evaporates from the ground.

High in the mountains the air is thinner than it is lower down, and the sunlight is more intense. Alpine plants take advantage of this to grow rapidly during warm weather. Their dark leaves absorb the infrared radiation (heat) from the Sun, so the plants are often a little warmer than the air around them.

MOUNTAIN HERBIVORES

Above the tree line in the Rocky Mountains, from Alaska to as far south as Oregon and Idaho, there lives an animal that is legendary for its sureness of foot. The mountain goat (*Oreamnos americanus*) climbs seemingly impossible cliffs, stands calmly on the narrowest of ledges and smallest pinnacles of rock, and leaps confidently from one rock to another. Its reputation is deserved, although mountain goats sometimes misjudge distances.

Mountain goat
Oreamnos americanus

Chamois
Rupicapra rupicapra

Japanese serow
Capricornis crispus

Wild goat
Capra aegragus

Urial
Ovis orientalis

Barbary sheep
Ammotragus lervia

They are not goats, but goat antelopes—close relatives of sheep and goats and part of the same subfamily (Caprinae), but with a rather stockier build so they look more like antelopes. All these animals belong to the family Bovidae, which also includes cattle.

Goat antelopes live in mountainous regions or in extremely harsh climates—the musk ox (*Ovibos moschatus*) of the Arctic is a goat antelope. In all, there are 26 species of goat antelopes; these include the wild goat (*Capra aegragus*), which is not a true goat, and the Barbary sheep (*Ammotragus lervia*), which is not a true sheep.

The chamois (*Rupicapra rupicapra*) is also a goat antelope. Smaller than the mountain goat, it lives in the mountains of Europe and the Middle East. In summer chamois graze on high alpine meadows, moving down the mountains in winter and feeding on mosses, lichens, and young tree shoots. Mountain goats have a similar diet.

Food is often scarce. Chamois can survive without food for up to two weeks; both they and mountain goats will fight to defend the resources on which they depend. Fights between mountain goats are rare—but very violent. Male chamois often fight.

Mountain goats are bulkier than chamois. Their coats are longer and shaggier, although in both species the coat consists of a thick, woolly layer next to the body, with an outer covering of coarse, stiff hair. Chamois are much nimbler than the slow-moving mountain goats. Like all goat antelopes, both female mountain goats and chamois live in small groups together with their young. Several individuals act as sentinels, or guards, while the others feed. Adult males, however, are usually solitary.

"Elephants" That Climb Trees

There are many smaller mammals that share the mountains with goat antelopes, and their appearances can be misleading.

Hyraxes (also called hyraces, conies, and dassies) look like rabbits and are sometimes mistaken for them. In the Bible they are called conies, a name that nowadays is sometimes applied to rabbits. They are about 20 inches (50 cm) long, much the same size as rabbits, with a short, stumpy tail and short, round ears. There are 11 species, and they live in Africa and the Middle East.

Rock and bush hyraxes live among rocks in the mountains. Tree hyraxes live in forests on mountainsides. All hyraxes climb well, and the forest-dwellers climb trees. All of them feed on plants, rock hyraxes eating mainly grass. They have difficulty maintaining a constant body

SMALL MAMMALS that live in the mountains of the Old World include a hare that changes the color of its coat to match the background in which it lives—of snow in winter and rock in summer. There are also hyraxes, animals related to the hoofed mammals, and marmots, social animals that dig burrows.

Johnston's hyrax
Procavia johnstoni

Arctic hare
Lepus timidus

Alpine marmot
Marmota marmota

A MALE PIKA sings its long call—a series of squeaks lasting up to 30 seconds—to announce its presence and warn off rivals. This is a North American pika (*Ochotona princeps*). Despite its rat-like appearance, it is related to rabbits and hares and is not a rodent.

Hares and Pikas

As one of its many names suggests, the arctic hare (*Lepus timidus*) inhabits the forests of the far north of America, Europe, and Asia. It really is a hare, although its ears are rather smaller than those of other hares. Small ears lose less body heat than big ears, so this is an adaptation to life in a cold climate. Another adaptation is its ability to change color to match the landscape. In the northern part of its range the arctic hare has a brown or gray-blue coat in summer and a white coat in winter. For this reason it is also known as the blue hare and varying hare. The hare can also be found farther south in mountains, where it is called the mountain hare. It can be found as far south as the Alps and Ireland—and is therefore sometimes called the Irish hare.

Pikas have small, round ears, short legs, and very short tails, and they are about 8 inches (20 cm) long. Although they look like rodents, or might be mistaken for guinea pigs, they actually belong to the same order (Lagomorpha) as the rabbits and hares. There are probably about 14 species of pikas, and they live in remote places in mountains and deserts. Two species occur in North America: the North American pika (*Ochotona princeps*) and the collared pika (*O. collaris*).

Pikas are vegetarians. In late summer they start collecting food for the winter. They gather grasses, sedges, leaves and stems of herbs, and any other available plant material, and they carry it to stores in their burrows or beneath overhanging rocks. This dries and turns into hay, on which they feed in winter.

When alarmed, pikas utter a series of short squeaks as a warning cry to alert others. Male

temperature and will huddle together or bask to warm themselves.

Hyraxes can be mistaken for guinea pigs as well as rabbits, and the name "hyrax" means "shrew-mouse," which is not an accurate description either. Hyraxes are hoofed animals. Some scientists believe they are related to modern elephants and sirenians (dugongs and manatees), others that they are related to horses, tapirs, and rhinoceroses.

pikas also "sing" a much longer call to declare their presence, mainly to rival males. Marmots are also highly vocal, whistling loudly if they feel threatened.

Unlike pikas, marmots are rodents. They are ground squirrels—often called woodchucks in North America—and many species, such as the alpine marmot (*Marmota marmota*) of southern Europe, live high in the mountains.

They are social animals, living in family groups of up to 15 individuals. They make their homes in burrows; sleeping is the thing they do best. Marmots hibernate at the first sign of winter, all of them making for the underground den and the last one in sealing the entrance. They remain there for six months, although they do wake every few weeks to urinate and defecate. Hibernation is a way of economizing on food. While they sleep, huddled together, their body temperatures fall to between 40°F and 45.5°F (4.5–7.5°C). Maintaining this temperature requires much less energy than a higher one.

MOUNTAIN CARNIVORES

Where there are small, plant-eating animals there are bigger animals that hunt them. Cats are the main enemy of hares, pikas, hyraxes, and marmots. Several species of small cat live in the mountains. The mountain lion (*Felis concolor*) will take prey the size of a small deer—or mountain goat.

The mountain lion is the biggest cat native to North America. It is also known as the Mexican lion, puma, cougar, eastern cougar, catamount, panther, Florida cougar, Florida

Lynx
Felis lynx

Bobcat
Felis rufus

panther, and painter. Some of these are local races or subspecies. The large number of names reflects the wide distribution of the species. The mountain cat is *F. jacobita*, an entirely different species. Also known as the Andean cat, it lives in the mountains of South America. It is much smaller than the mountain lion—its body is up to 30 inches (76 cm) long, compared with an average 70 inches (178 cm) for a mountain lion—and it hunts small mammals and birds.

Like most cats, the mountain lion stalks its prey and pounces as soon as it is close enough, and it will eat any animal it can catch. It hunts within a range, males having larger ranges than females, and summer ranges being bigger than winter ranges, although ranges often overlap. In summer a male hunts in an area of up to 112 square miles (290 sq. km), and a female up to 80 square miles (207 sq. km). Winter ranges are about half these sizes and occupy lower elevations, because when snow covers the alpine meadows, the larger grazing mammals that are

TWO SMALL CATS of North America. The lynx is easily recognized by its prominent ear tufts, the bobcat by its distinctive markings, and both cats by their short tails. Both hunt mainly by night, although in winter the bobcat is sometimes active by day. Only the bobcat is exclusively American. The lynx also occurs in northern Europe and Asia.

THE MOUNTAIN LION, or cougar *(Felis concolor)*, is at home in the mountains, but it also lives in the forests and deserts of North and South America.

their main prey move down into the valleys.

The bobcat (*F. rufus*) is found from southern Canada to Mexico. It is a powerful animal with a body up to 40 inches (102 cm) long and weighing up to 66 pounds (30 kg). Its brown coat with black spots disguises it well against the rocks and dense vegetation where it hunts cottontails. Cottontails are its most important food, but it is also capable of attacking a small deer, or a sheep or goat.

The bobcat is similar in size and overall shape to the lynx (*F. lynx*), an animal that occurs across northern Europe and Asia as well as North America. Its coat is often a plain gray-brown, but the color and patterning are quite variable. In Europe and Asia, where there are no bobcats, many lynxes have spotted coats. Both bobcats and lynxes hunt on the ground at night, although they will climb trees.

Lynxes live much farther north than bobcats, and their bodies equip them for life in a colder climate. They have shorter tails than bobcats— 2–7 inches (5–18 cm), compared with 4–8 inches (10–20 cm). Short tails lose less body heat than long tails. They also have longer legs, which allow them to move more easily in deep snow.

BIRDS OF THE MOUNTAINS

Circling slowly, almost lazily, high in the clear blue sky, the golden eagle (*Aquila chrysaetos*) is one of the most magnificent of birds. It is a rare sight, but only because golden eagles inhabit remote mountains and moors and hunt by patrolling a very large area. In fact, the golden eagle is probably the most common eagle in the world. It occurs throughout most of the Northern Hemisphere as far south as Mexico and North Africa.

It is a large bird, measuring about 30 to 35 inches (76 to 89 cm) long and with a wingspan of up to 6.5 feet (2 m). It really is "eagle-eyed." Watching from high in the air, it is well able to see the smallest movement on the ground, and no hare, rabbit, or ground-dwelling bird can escape its notice. Its attack begins with a steep, fast dive, and it usually feeds on the ground.

The lammergeier, or bearded vulture (*Gypaetus barbatus*), is bigger than the golden eagle—37–41 inches (95–105 cm) long—and even more magnificent, with black wings and a golden body. It inhabits mountains in various parts of southern Europe, Africa, and Asia, but nowhere is it common. It is a vulture and feeds on carrion (dead and rotting flesh), and it spends most of its time in the air. Although it is bigger than the golden eagle, it is smaller than most of the vultures it encounters, and it allows them to feed first. This often leaves it with just the bones. It drops these onto rocks to break them open so it can eat the marrow.

Isidor's crested eagle, or the black-and-chestnut eagle (*Oroaetus isidori*), lives in the

Andes from Colombia south to Bolivia. It is also a large bird, about the size of a golden eagle, but its hunting technique is different. This eagle flies low over the mountain forests, catching any bird or mammal up to the size of a porcupine (18 inches, 46 cm, long). It frequently catches monkeys.

THE LAMMERGEIER, or bearded vulture (*Gypaetus barbatus*), lives in mountains from southern Europe to India.

Choughs, Sunbirds, and Snow Finches

Choughs belong to the crow family (Corvidae), birds renowned for their intelligence and versatility in exploiting any opportunity. Most are birds of forests and farmland, but the choughs live near coasts, nesting on sea cliffs, and in the mountains of the Old World (Europe, Asia, and Africa). In the Himalayas they can be found at heights of up to 27,000 feet (8,000 m).

There are two species. Both are about the size of pigeons. The chough (*Pyrrhocorax pyrrhocorax*) is a glossy blue-black and has a long, slightly curved bill. The bill and legs of young birds are yellow, and those of adults are

Isidor's crested eagle
Oroaetus isidori

Golden eagle
Aquila chrysaetos

**MOUNTAIN BIRDS
feed on plants,
nectar, and insects.
Close relatives of
lowland species, they
are fully adapted to
life in the mountains.**

Snow finch
Montifringilla nivalis

Chough
Pyrrhocorax pyrrhocorax

Alpine chough
P. graculus

Malachite sunbird
Nectarinia famosa

red. The alpine chough (*P. graculus*) is black, with a shorter yellow bill and red legs. It lives at higher altitudes than *P. pyrrhocorax*.

Sunbirds live in the Old World tropics, where they are the counterparts of the hummingbirds of America, feeding on nectar and pollinating plants as hummingbirds do. They are small, or very small, brightly colored birds. There are 116 species of them, comprising the family Nectariniidae, of which 76 species are African. The malachite sunbird (*Nectarinia famosa*) lives high in the mountains of East Africa.

Snow finches (*Montifringilla nivalis*) are the size of large house sparrows, which they resemble and to which they are related. They eat seeds and insects. Unlike sparrows, they live and nest on the ground. True mountain birds, they live above the snow line in the European Alps and mountains of Asia.

A HAY MEADOW IN THE ALPS *(opposite)* **growing vetch and vetchling. These plants grow between 5,000 and 6,000 feet (1,500 and 2,000 m) above sea level. The meadows are used for winter pasture.**

ALPINE MEADOWS

Above about 5,000 feet (1,500 m) the natural forest in the Alps begins to consist mainly of coniferous trees, especially silver fir (*Abies alba*), Norway spruce (*Picea abies*), and European larch (*Larix decidua*). In many places, though, the natural forest has been cleared to provide winter pasture for cattle and sheep. The grasses and herbs are also cut to make hay.

In spring and early summer the hay meadows of the Alps are filled with a dazzling array of flowers. In summer the weather is often very hot on the exposed slopes, but the winters are cold and long. Soils are thin and contain only small amounts of plant nutrients, and water drains quickly from them so they are often dry. Despite the poor conditions, many species of herbs have established themselves. They are

small, many have stems and leaves that spread to form mats, and they produce flowers and set seed during the short growing season. They all flower at the same time, which is why the meadows are so colorful.

Yellows predominate, but there are also the deep blue of the gentians (*Gentiana* species) and paler blues of bellflowers (*Campanula* species) and viper's bugloss (*Echium vulgare*). Orchids thrive in the meadows and occur in many colors.

Hay meadows are confined to the lower slopes—and also the gentler slopes, which makes them accessible to walkers as well as farm livestock. Trees grow on the steeper slopes, their roots helping to bind the soil together and prevent erosion. Above 6,000 feet (2,000 m) on the sunny, south-facing slopes there are still meadows, but they are not cut for hay. These extend to nearly 10,000 feet (3,000 m) and are used only for summer grazing. At this altitude the winter weather is much too severe for farm animals, which have to be brought farther down the mountains.

The high meadows also contain many of the colorful flowering plants found in the hay meadows, but they tend to be smaller. Heavy grazing throughout the growing season and the incessant wind that chills and dries them prevent them from growing to the size they attain at lower levels. Above these meadows the grassland is gradually reduced to patches among the bare rock, and finally it disappears,

Components of the ecosystem

1 Sedge
2 Orchid
3 Groundsel
4 Plantain
5 Grass
6 Chamois
7 Yellowhammer
8 Marmot
9 Root-living aphid
10 Peregrine falcon
11 Gray wolf
12 Gray-headed woodpecker
13 Yellow-hill ant in ant-hill

Energy flow

⟹ Primary producer/primary consumer
➡ Primary/secondary consumer
⟹ Secondary/tertiary consumer

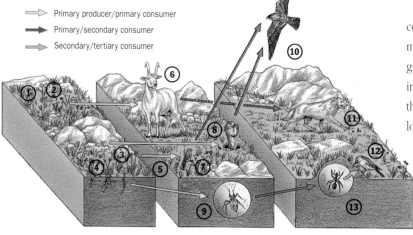

Primary producers   Herbivores   Carnivores

AN ALPINE MEADOW ECOSYSTEM. Winter snow forces many animals to hibernate or migrate down the mountain in search of food.

although some flowers, such as saxifrages and toadflaxes, survive even there, rooted in sheltered crevices.

The Meadow Ecosystem

Once the short growing season ends, the nutritional value of the plants deteriorates fairly quickly, then the snow starts to fall. It is not only the farm animals that move to areas lower down in winter. So do many of the animals that feed on plants.

The Alps are home to the chamois (see page 37–38) and also to the ibex (*Capra ibex*). Like the chamois, the ibex is also a goat antelope, with long, thick horns that curve backward, and it lives above the tree line, grazing in the meadows and descending into the forest only in the harshest winter weather. Ibex were hunted almost to extinction and survive now only in a few reserves where they are protected. Marmots (see pages 38 and 40) burrow in the alpine meadows.

The biggest grazing mammal in the meadows is the elk, or wapiti, known in Britain as the red deer (*Cervus elaphus*). Elk thrive in many areas because their natural predators have become rare. When herds of elk become too large, they can damage vegetation and kill young trees by eating their shoots.

HUNTERS OF THE HIGH MEADOWS

Wolves are the natural predators of all the large alpine mammals. The gray wolf (*Canis lupus*) lives in the remote places of North America and Europe, in the tundra, in dense forests, and in the mountains. In Europe, where there are no large cats to compete with them for prey, wolves are the only predators of animals the size of chamois, ibex, and elk. Unfortunately, they cannot distinguish wild sheep and goats from domesticated ones, and their assaults on farm animals—and occasionally the humans tending them—have led to their persecution.

Birds of prey have also been persecuted, but in many places they are now protected. Golden eagles and lammergeiers (see page 42) are no longer hunted. Neither is a smaller but more spectacular aerial hunter, the peregrine falcon, or duck hawk (*Falco peregrinus*).

The peregrine is not a large bird. It is 15–20 inches (38–51 cm) long, about the size of a crow, and it spends much of its time perched on a high vantage point, from where it watches for prey. It hunts birds by diving almost vertically at more than 60 mph (96.5 km/h) and seizing its victim with its sharp talons. Usually, the first strike kills the prey outright. If the victim sees the falcon approaching and tries to evade it, the peregrine will give chase. It can out-maneuver and overtake most birds.

AMPHIBIANS OF JAPAN.
Both the Japanese giant salamander and the Japanese tree frog are adapted for life in cold mountain streams.

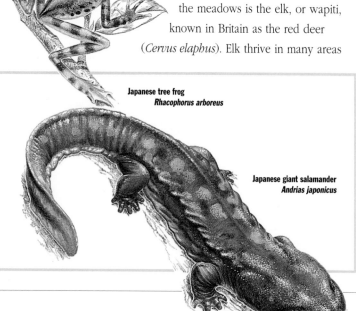

Japanese tree frog
Rhacophorus arboreus

Japanese giant salamander
Andrias japonicus

Peregrine falcon
Falco peregrinus

Gray wolf
Canis lupus

Frogs and Salamanders

There are also less clearly visible hunters. All adult frogs are meat-eaters. Most hunt insects and other small invertebrates, but bigger frogs catch larger animals, including fish and even rodents. Frogs are most abundant in warm climates, but they are very adaptable, and some live in the mountains.

Japanese tree frogs (*Rhacophorus arboreus*) inhabit the forests that cloak the mountains of Japan. They belong to the family of Old World tree frogs (Rhacophoridae) and, like other tree frogs, have suction pads on the end of their fingers that help them grip leaves and branches. They lay their eggs above water in a mass of foam—this keeps them moist. When they hatch, the tadpoles drop out of the foam into the water.

Like frogs, salamanders begin their lives as aquatic larvae, and move onto land as adults. There are exceptions, however, and some salamanders retain a number of juvenile features all their lives and continue living in water.

One of these is the Japanese giant salamander (*Andrias japonicus*). It is one of three species of giant salamanders in the family Cryptobranchidae. One of the other species lives in China, the other in North America. The Japanese giant salamander lives at altitudes between 1,000 and 3,000 feet (300 and 900 m) in the cold mountain streams on the islands of Kyushu and Honshu. It has a diet of invertebrate animals, fish, and other small animals.

It has the distinction of being the biggest salamander in the world—individuals can grow to a length of 5 feet (1.5 m). In captivity they have been known to live for more than 50 years.

HIGHLAND PREDATORS include the peregrine falcon, which roosts and nests on narrow ledges on cliffs, and the gray wolf. The sequence of illustrations *(top)* shows a peregrine attack on a wood pigeon. Wolves make their dens in natural hollows where there is some shelter from the wind, but near a vantage point that gives them a clear view of the surrounding countryside.

THE HIGH PLATEAU

Above the meadows there is often a region of fairly level ground, a high plateau. It is a cold, bleak, and usually wet place, but it is not barren. There are grasses, small shrubs such as willows (*Salix* species), and black crowberry (*Empetrum nigrum*). In wetter places there may be cotton grasses (*Eriophorum* species) and sedges (*Carex* species). On the high plateaux of Europe there is often heather (*Calluna vulgaris*) and gorse (*Ulex* species).

This vegetation is similar to that of a heath, and so are the animals. There are many insects; birds that hunt them include the wheatear (*Oenanthe oenanthe*) and, in the Old World, the stonechat (*Saxicola torquata*). There are small rodents, hares, and pikas—the large-eared pika (*Ochotona macrotis*) of the Himalayas lives 7,500–20,000 feet (2,300–6,100 m) above sea level. Mountain goats, chamois, ibex, and other goat antelopes may spend time grazing there.

Falcons and other birds of prey hunt the small animals, and in Africa and Asia the Old World counterpart of the mountain lion may stalk larger prey. The leopard (*Panthera pardus*) is bigger than a mountain lion, but otherwise very similar. It lives alone and is active by both day and night, except where it has been persecuted and hides during the day. Like most cats it will feed on carrion and, if its meal is likely to be disturbed, it will carry food into a tree, sometimes leaving it there to eat later. It climbs and swims well.

High in the Himalayas and the mountains surrounding them in Afghanistan, Russia, and China the snow leopard, or ounce (*Panthera uncia*), hunts mammals up to the size of sheep and goats as well as ground-nesting birds. It spends the summer in the alpine meadows and high plateaux, near the permanent snow line, sometimes at heights of above 19,000 feet (6,000 m). In winter it follows its prey down the mountain, but rarely descends below about 6,500 feet (2,000 m). Hair on its paws forms a cushion on the underside. This increases the surface area, making it easier for the snow leopard to move across snow, and it also provides insulation. Its coat grows thick in winter also for insulation, but it is thin in summer.

Prey is distributed sparsely at high altitudes, and the snow leopard hunts over a range of more than 30 square miles (78 sq. km). It is a powerful hunter, stalking its

Components of the ecosystem

1 Dwarf gorse
2 Heather, heath
3 Woodrush
4 Grasses
5 Broom
6 Insects feeding on heather
7 Short-tailed vole
8 Rabbit
9 Wheatear
10 Kestrel
11 Stonechat
12 Violet ground beetle
13 Red ant
14 Adder

Energy flow

⇨ Primary producer/
    primary consumer

➡ Primary/secondary
    consumer

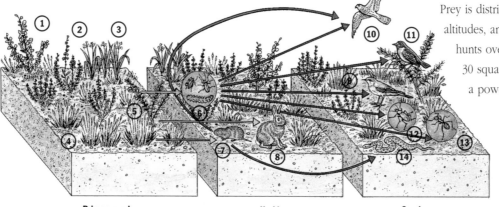

Primary producers   Herbivores   Carnivores

**A HEATHLAND
ECOSYSTEM. Small
mammals feeding on low
plants and shrubs
provide good hunting for
birds of prey.**

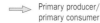

prey and launching its attack from a distance of up to 50 feet (15 m).

For many years their skins commanded high prices in the fur trade, and snow leopard numbers fell drastically as a result of hunting. This beautiful cat is rare in many places where once it was firmly established. Now, however, it is illegal to buy or sell the skin of a snow leopard; such legislation may allow its populations to recover.

TWO SMALL BIRDS OF THE MOUNTAINS. The stonechat is smaller than a sparrow. It nests on the ground, feeds on insects, and is found in western and southern Europe and the Middle East. The wheatear is slightly larger. It occurs throughout Europe, Asia, and in parts of Greenland, northern Canada, and Alaska.

Stonechat
Saxicola torquata

Wheatear
Oenanthe oenanthe

THE LEOPARD is a hunter on the high grasslands in mountains of the Old World tropics and subtropics.

Leopard
Panthera pardus

Survival of the Mountains

Tall, imposing, and made from hard, solid rock, mountains seem indestructible. They look as though they have stood from the beginning of time exactly where they stand today. Yet mountains do disappear—very slowly they are worn away. But as old mountains are reduced to level plains, new mountains are thrust skyward.

TYPES OF MASS WASTING. Sliding rocks slump when they tip backward as they move down-slope. An earthflow can be triggered by heavy rain; the slipping rocks can break into steps. In a mudflow the saturated earth flows down even a gentle slope. Soil creep is much slower and is revealed by displaced trees and soil.

Wind and water are the agents by which mountains are gradually worn away. The process takes many thousands of years, but it is unceasing. When a mountain loses rocks or soil through erosion, the process is called mass wasting. This can happen in several ways. Rock falls and slides, or landslides (see page 28), leave obvious traces in the form of scree or piles of rocks. Other types of mass wasting are often more serious.

Every year, in every mountain range in the world, there are landslides that destroy homes and kill people. The table (opposite below) lists some of the major disasters, but there have been many more. Between June and August of 1997, for example, landslides in different areas of India killed about 950 people.

It is water that causes rocks and earth to slide downhill, by lubricating a layer—often of clay—below the surface. Material above the lubricated layer starts to float away, then slides; once it has begun to slide, it accelerates and carries away more material from farther down the slope. Often the base of the sliding earth or rock moves a little faster than material above it, which is not lubricated. This causes the sliding mass to tip backward as a rotational "slump."

Sometimes an entire surface of earth mixed with rocks can become detached in sections. This produces an "earthflow," in which the mixture breaks into steps, the bottom step piling up as a "toe" against the more solid surface that halts the slide.

Where the side of a mountain or hill is covered by a layer of fine soil, heavy rain can turn much of it into mud. This flows like a liquid, first into the nearest valley and then down the valley, collecting material from the valley sides all the way. It will move down even a gentle slope, but once it starts moving, it accelerates and cannot be stopped. If there are people living in its path in the lower part of the valley, the consequences can be catastrophic.

These types of mass wasting happen suddenly and are spectacular, but they are not what destroy mountains. Mountains disappear by a process so gradual it is difficult to observe. The process is called soil creep. Every time it rains heavily, or the winter covering of snow

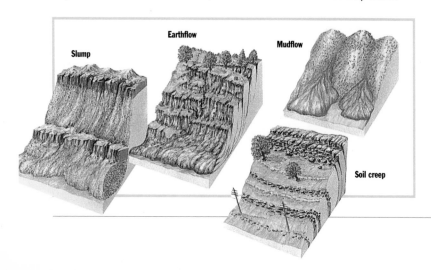

Slump

Earthflow

Mudflow

Soil creep

TOURIST NUMBERS can detract from the character of wilderness areas through the construction of roads and provision of facilities. This bus party is visiting Mount McKinley, in Denali National Park, Alaska. It is the highest peak in North America.

the surface at all, but simply rolled along it. Rolling and falling particles collide with others and dislodge them. As with the effect of water, the result is to move soil a very short distance. Wind can blow uphill as well as downhill, of course, but because of gravity the general effect is to move soil downhill. Gravity pulls objects toward the center of the Earth. Therefore, even if particles are being blown uphill, when they fall, the force acting on them pulls them part way downhill again.

The amount of movement is very small, but it is repeated with every heavy fall of rain and every strong wind. Evidence for it can sometimes be found in the depth of the soil. This is usually greater at the bottom of a slope than at the top. Field walls and fences that were built in straight

thaws rapidly, water flows downhill. As it flows, the water gathers small soil particles and carries them a short distance down the slope. They are constantly being picked up and dropped, but the overall effect is that a large amount of soil is moved a very short way downhill.

At other times strong winds will lift particles from soil that is dry. Again, most of them travel only a short way before falling back to the surface, and many of them are not raised from

MAJOR LANDSLIDES OF RECENT YEARS

Torrential rainfall is a common cause of landslides, but they can be triggered by other events. In 1920 earthquakes started the catastrophic landslides in the loess region of northern China that cost some 200,000 lives.

Year	Location	Deaths
1988	Brazil	280+*
1989	Sri Lanka	300+*
1990	Indonesia	130+*
1991	Malawi	500+*
1992	India	230+*
1993	Honduras	400
1994	Colombia	up to 1,000
1995	Afghanistan	354
1997	Peru	300
1998	Honduras	5,637+

Fatalities from floods and landslides

lines across the slope (at right angles to the direction of the slope) become crooked because soil does not move at the same rate everywhere.

Creep acts slowly, but over thousands of years it is the process that carries away entire mountain ranges, eventually to the sea.

Damage from Wheels and Feet

Mount Everest is strewn with litter. Many mountaineering parties have attempted to climb it, and most of them have left behind the empty containers, especially oxygen bottles, in which they carried their supplies. This behavior is understandable. Climbing Everest imposes huge physical strains, and it is hard to justify carrying items for which there is no longer any use. Nevertheless, the problem has grown so serious that the Nepalese authorities now require mountaineers to bring their garbage off the mountain and dispose of it properly, and teams of mountaineers have volunteered to clean up as much as they can.

This is an extreme case—Everest is the world's most famous mountain—but the scenery in many mountain areas now bears scars from the large number of people who visit them. Mountains are popular. Visitors need roads and parking spaces to provide access, and where there are roads, there may be pressure to provide rest rooms, restaurants, souvenir shops, information centers, and other facilities.

Off the roads most walkers follow well-marked footpaths. These can be eroded by wear from too many boots. The path becomes uneven, with a deep gully in the center, and in wet weather it is muddy and slippery. Then walkers keep to the side of the eroded path, where the walking is more comfortable. This extends the eroded area. In very popular areas whole hillsides can be seriously damaged in this way.

Fortunately, the damage can be repaired. This means closing the eroded area while hollows are filled in and planted with local vegetation. Alternative routes allow people to continue visiting the area, and providing several paths reduces the pressure on each.

Rock climbers can also cause damage. It is easy to dislodge loose rocks accidentally; when this happens, the falling rocks tend to take a few more rocks with them. Experienced climbers are careful to avoid damage of this kind, not least because of the danger to anyone who may be below—but it does happen. Hammering rocks to fix attachments for ropes can open up cracks beneath the surface so that at some later time sections of the rock face fall away.

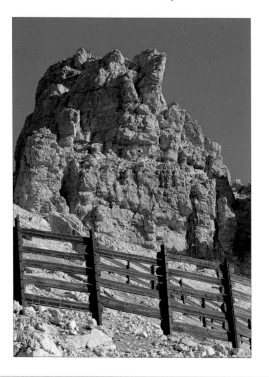

AN AVALANCHE OF SNOW can carry away power lines, destroy buildings and roads, and kill anyone in its path. Sometimes avalanches are triggered deliberately by explosives in order to remove excess snow safely under controlled conditions.

AN ANTI-AVALANCHE FENCE near Cortina d'Ampezzo, Italy, appears as just an ordinary fence in summer, but in winter it holds back the snow, preventing it from falling as an avalanche onto roads and buildings.

AVALANCHE

Falls of rock are dangerous, but rare. Falls of snow are very common, and they are even more dangerous. Every winter there are thousands of avalanches in the European Alps. (Most, not all, occur at very high altitudes and harm no one.)

Snow collects in natural hollows and on shaded slopes. On steep slopes or slopes covered with grass that makes them slippery, snow will not accumulate; its weight makes it slide away harmlessly. On very shallow slopes the snow can accumulate to a great thickness, but will not fall. The danger is from snow lying on a gradient of about 30° to 40°. This is neither steep enough to make the snow fall while the layer is still thin nor shallow enough to prevent even a thick layer from moving.

A large fall of snow may increase the weight of the layer. A sudden warming early in spring or from a föhn wind (see page 36) may melt some of the snow higher up so water flows downhill and beneath the thick layer, loosening and lubricating it. These conditions may not be enough to start the snow moving, but they will make it very unstable. Then the smallest vibration may dislodge it. The whoosh of a passing skier, the snapping of the branch of a tree, or a gunshot, may be all that is needed. Once the snow starts moving, it accelerates and gathers more snow. This is an avalanche.

Its movement also generates a wind. In a major avalanche the wind can reach 185 mph (300 km/h). This alone will cause serious structural damage to buildings. The avalanche itself may be half a mile (800 m) across, move at

100 mph (160 km/h), and travel more than 1 mile (1.6 km) before the snow comes to rest.

Avalanches are much less of a risk to life and property than they used to be. Mountain patrols detect snow accumulations before they become dangerous, and explosives can be used to clear snow safely. Strong fences are built across slopes where avalanches are likely.

CONTROLLING WATER in a mountain valley. In flood a mountain stream loaded with soil and debris can become a destructive force. A number of devices can slow its rate and limit erosion.

REDUCING EROSION

Mountain erosion is a natural process that cannot be eliminated, but it can be controlled. A first step is to reduce the erosion we cause ourselves. Trees have been cleared from many mountainsides to provide land for farming or to create ski slopes. Trees bind the soil, reducing soil creep, landslides, and mudslides, and they hold snow, reducing the risk of avalanches.

If trees must be removed—and sometimes they must—other ways must be found to hold soil and snow. Snow fences are widely used, and they are effective. Soil can be kept inside cultivated fields if these are terraced so that each field is approximately horizontal. Terracing is traditional in most mountainous regions.

Controlling Water

Flowing water is the main agent of erosion. Any measure that slows it is valuable because the faster water flows, the more energy it has and the more soil it can carry.

Planting trees to hold soil and to slow the downhill movement of water is a first step in reducing soil erosion. Exposed rocks on steep slopes can be held in place by netting. Steep, soil-covered slopes can also be terraced not to make fields but to reduce the gradient.

Small dams halt the flow of water. A small lake fills, then water spills over the dam and across an area enclosed by a wall. Here, the water moves slowly, and particles settle out from it. Where a stream is eroding its banks, these can be protected. A series of dams, areas where sediment can settle, and protected banks will do much to slow the rate of erosion on mountainsides.

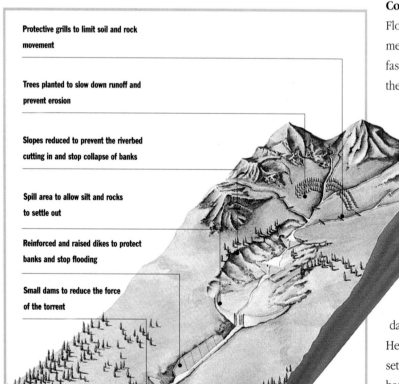

Protective grills to limit soil and rock movement

Trees planted to slow down runoff and prevent erosion

Slopes reduced to prevent the riverbed cutting in and stop collapse of banks

Spill area to allow silt and rocks to settle out

Reinforced and raised dikes to protect banks and stop flooding

Small dams to reduce the force of the torrent

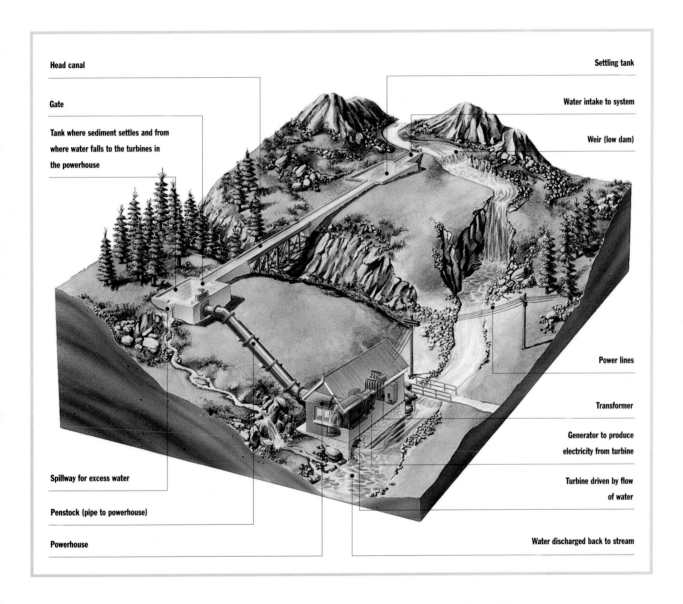

Head canal

Gate

Tank where sediment settles and from
where water falls to the turbines in
the powerhouse

Spillway for excess water

Penstock (pipe to powerhouse)

Powerhouse

Settling tank

Water intake to system

Weir (low dam)

Power lines

Transformer

Generator to produce
electricity from turbine

Turbine driven by flow
of water

Water discharged back to stream

Even grass helps. A dense growth of tough grass that tolerates flooding can turn a torrent into a broad, gentle stream. This technique is often used to restore badly eroded gullies.

On some sites it is possible to combine control of the water with generating power. Water is diverted from a stream and stored in tanks, where the sediment that might damage machinery settles to the bottom. The force of the water down a steep slope to the powerhouse spins a turbine. This drives the generator, producing electrical power.

A hydroelectric plant of this kind causes no pollution and does not alter the water in any way. It merely extracts energy from it, and that helps to reduce the erosion the water can cause.

HYDROELECTRIC POWER on a small scale. In the tanks sediment that might damage machinery settles to the bottom. Many schemes like this have been built in China to generate power for rural communities.

Glossary

alga A simple green plant that lacks true leaves, stem, and root. Many algae are single-celled; some are multicelled. Seaweeds are algae.

amphibian A vertebrate animal of the class Amphibia. The young develop in water, although the adults may live on land. Frogs, toads, newts, and salamanders are amphibians.

asthenosphere A region of the upper mantle in which the rock behaves like a solid that can be squeezed until it spreads and flows. The asthenosphere lies beneath the lithosphere, its upper margin about 60 miles (100 km) below the surface and its lower margin about 250 miles (400 km) below the surface.

bacteria Microscopic organisms, most of which are single-celled, that are found in air, water, and soil everywhere. Different types vary in shape and way of life.

biome A large region throughout which living conditions for plants and animals are broadly similar, so the region can be classified according to its vegetation type.

bora A cold, dry, northeasterly wind that blows down the mountains to the east of the Adriatic, most commonly in winter.

carnivore An animal that feeds exclusively on other animals.

carrion Animal flesh that has started to decay.

consumer An organism that is unable to manufacture its own food from simple ingredients but must obtain it by eating (consuming) other organisms.

continental crust The rocks forming the crustal plates that bear continents and continental shelves. The rock is less dense than oceanic crust and therefore occupies a greater volume, which is why it projects above the ocean surface. Continental crust is mostly 19–25 miles (30–40 km) thick, but up to 43 miles (70 km) thick beneath mountain ranges.

convection Transfer of heat through a liquid or gas by the movement of the liquid or gas.

core The central part of the Earth, comprising a solid inner core with a diameter of about 1,550 miles (2,500 km) surrounded by a liquid outer core about 1,380 miles (2,220 km) thick.

crust The rock that makes up the outermost layer of the solid Earth, varying in thickness from about 3 miles (5 km) beneath some parts of the oceans to about 43 miles (70 km) beneath mountain ranges.

ecology The study of the relationships among living organisms in a defined area and between the organisms and the nonliving features of their surroundings.

ecosystem A community of living organisms and their nonliving environment within a defined area. This may be of any size. A forest may be studied as an ecosystem and so may a drop of water.

elfin woodland Woodland consisting of dwarfed, gnarled trees, often festooned with lichens, that grows near the tree line on tropical mountainsides.

epicenter The point on the surface of the Earth that lies directly above the place where an earthquake originates (the focus or hypocenter).

eutrophic Highly enriched in nutrients.

fault A naturally occurring fracture in a rock mass where the resulting rock bodies have moved in relation to each other.

fire fountain A plume of hot lava thrown into the air during a volcanic eruption, due to the rapid expansion of gases as they escape from the rising magma. Fire fountains are characteristic of the Hawaiian type of eruption. They are also called lava fountains.

focus The place, below the surface, where an earthquake originates. It is also called the hypocenter.

föhn wind A warm, dry wind that blows down the side of a mountain. It is caused by air flowing over the mountain, cooling and losing its moisture as it rises up the windward side, then sinking and warming down the lee side. The chinook wind, on the eastern side of the Rocky Mountains, is of this type.

geothermal gradient The rate at which the temperature rises with increasing depth below the surface of the Earth. It averages 87°F per mile (30°C per km) but varies widely.

gill 1 The organ with which an aquatic animal obtains oxygen from water. It consists of thin membranes with a large surface area over which water flows. Oxygen passes from the water through the walls of blood vessels in the gill membrane and into the blood. Most aquatic animals have two gills. **2** A bladelike structure in the fruiting body of a fungus (often the visible stage in the life of the fungus, such as a toadstool or mushroom) from which spores are released.

glacier A layer of ice made by the compression of snow due to the weight of overlying snow that accumulates year after year. Most glaciers spread by flowing. A glacier covering a wide area is called an "ice sheet;" one confined by the sides of a valley is called a "valley glacier."

graben A block of rock that has been depressed with respect to the blocks of rock to either side.

ground water Water below ground that fills all the spaces between soil particles, thus saturating the soil.

Gutenberg Discontinuity The boundary between the mantle and outer core of the Earth, 1,800 miles (2,900 km) below the surface.

herbivore An animal that feeds exclusively on plants.

hibernation A strategy for surviving the winter by entering a deep sleep during which the heart beat, rate of respiration, and metabolic rate of an animal slow dramatically, and its body temperature falls to within a few degrees of the air temperature. The hibernating animal maintains its vital functions by metabolizing food reserves stored in its body during late summer.

horst A block of rock that has been raised in relation to the blocks on either side.

insectivore An animal that feeds mainly or exclusively on insects.

invertebrate An animal that does not have a backbone.

lapse rate The rate at which air temperature decreases with increasing altitude. The average lapse rate is 3.5°F per 1,000 feet (6.5°C per km).

lava Molten rock that erupts from a volcano and the solid rock that forms when lava cools.

lava fountain *See* fire fountain.

lichen A plantlike organism consisting of a fungus and either an alga or a cyanobacterium (a bacterium that carries out photosynthesis) living in close association. The visible part of a lichen may be crustlike, scaly, leafy, or shrubby.

lithosphere The outermost part of the solid Earth, comprising the rocks of the crust and the uppermost mantle. Its thickness ranges from 1 mile (1.6 km) or less at ocean ridges to 90 miles (145 km) beneath old ocean crust and 185 miles (298 km) beneath continents.

lung The organ of respiration in air-breathing vertebrates. In land-dwelling mollusks (snails and slugs), the part of the body involved in respiration.

magma Molten rock produced by the melting of the lower part of the crust or upper part of the mantle.

mantle The region of the Earth lying between the crust and the core.

mass wasting The movement of rock or earth down a slope under the influence of gravity.

Mohorovičić Discontinuity The boundary between the crust and mantle, at depths ranging from about 3 miles (5 km) beneath some parts of the ocean floor and 43 miles (70 km) beneath some mountain ranges.

nuée ardente A fast-flowing cloud of hot gases and dust, sometimes incandescent (the name means "glowing cloud") emitted during some types of volcanic eruption.

oceanic crust The rocks that lie beneath the oceans, forming several distinct layers with a total thickness averaging about 3 miles (5 km).

omnivore An animal that eats food derived from both plants and animals.

parasite An organism that lives on the surface or inside the body of another organism. The parasite is usually smaller than its host and gets food, shelter, or some other necessity from it. The effects of the parasite on its host may range from none at all to severe illness or even death.

photosynthesis The series of chemical reactions by which green plants manufacture sugars, obtaining hydrogen from water and carbon from carbon dioxide, the energy driving the reactions being provided by light that is absorbed by chlorophyll.

phytoplankton *See* plankton

plankton The small organisms that live near the surface of water and drift with movements of the water.

They include single-celled plants (phytoplankton) and small animals (zooplankton), some of which are the larvae of fish and crustaceans.

plate tectonics The theory that the crust of the Earth is made up of a number of solid sections, called plates, that move in relation to each other. This explains continental drift and the spreading of the sea floors.

predator An organism that obtains food by consuming another organism. Most predators are animals that chase, overpower, and kill their prey, but insectivorous plants are also predators.

producer An organism, such as a green plant, that assembles large, complex substances from simple ingredients. These may then be eaten by consumers. On land the principal producers are green plants and in water they are phytoplankton (*see* plankton).

pyroclastics Rocks ejected during a volcanic eruption.

respiration 1 The oxidation of carbon to carbon dioxide in cells with the release of energy. **2** The action of breathing.

ridge 1 A linear hill with a sharply defined crest. **2** (mid-ocean ridge) A linear feature on the ocean floor where two plates are moving apart, and new material is rising from the mantle. **3** A linear projection from a region of high atmospheric pressure.

scree Loose rock on the lower part of a slope that has become detached from the side of a hill or mountain and moved down the slope under the influence of gravity to accumulate near the bottom.

sea mount An isolated hill on the sea bed.

seismic wave A wave that travels through the solid Earth. Seismic waves caused by earthquakes are detected and recorded at widely separated points on the surface, allowing the magnitude and focus of the earthquake to be calculated.

soil creep The gradual gravitational movement of soil down a slope. It is a form of mass wasting.

subduction The sinking of one crustal plate beneath another made from rock that is less dense.

transpiration The loss of water vapor through pores, called stomata in the leaves and lenticels in the stems, of green plants.

tree line The climatic limit beyond which trees are unable to grow.

trench A deep depression in the ocean floor where one crustal plate is being subducted beneath another.

tropics Those parts of the world that lie between latitudes 23°30'N and 23°30'S. These latitudes mark the boundaries of the region within which the Sun is directly overhead at noon on at least one day each year. The Tropic of Cancer is to the north of the equator and the Tropic of Capricorn to the south.

vertebrate An animal that has a backbone. Vertebrates also have a bony skull containing the brain and a skeleton made from bone or cartilage. Fish, amphibians, reptiles, birds, and mammals are vertebrates.

water table The uppermost margin of the ground water, below which the soil is saturated and above which it is not, although it is wet.

zooplankton *See* plankton.

Further Reading

Basics of Environmental Science by Michael Allaby. Routledge.

Biology by Neil A. Campbell. The Benjamin/Cummings Publishing Co. Inc.

The Encyclopedia of Birds edited by Christopher M. Perrins and Alex L.A. Middleton. Facts on File.

The Encyclopedia of Insects edited by Christopher O'Toole. Facts on File.

The Encyclopedia of Mammals edited by David Macdonald. Facts on File.

The Encyclopedia of Reptiles and Amphibians edited by Tim Halliday and Kraig Adler. Facts on File.

Flowering Plants of the World edited by V.H. Heywood. Oxford University Press, New York.

Green Planet edited by David M. Moore. Cambridge University Press.

The Hunters by Philip Whitfield. Simon and Schuster.

Hutchinson Encyclopedia of the Earth edited by Peter J. Smith. Hutchinson.

The Lie of the Land edited by K.J. Gregory. Oxford University Press, New York.

Longman Illustrated Animal Encyclopedia edited by Philip Whitfield. Guild Publishing.

The Oxford Encyclopedia of Trees of the World edited by Bayard Hora. Oxford University Press, New York.

Planet Earth: Cosmology, Geology, and the Evolution of Life and Environment by Cesare Emiliani. Cambridge University Press.

Snakes of the World by Chris Mattison. Blandford Press Ltd.

The Science of Ecology by Richard Brewer. Saunders College Publishing, Harcourt Brace College Publishers.

Photographic Acknowledgments

9 Powerstock/Zefa Photo Library; **10–11** David Parker/Science Photo Library; **13** Powerstock/Zefa Photo Library; **16** Gerald Cubitt; **18–19** Victor Englebert; **21** Jiji Tsushin/The Press Association; **23** Frank Spooner Pictures; **25** Keith Gunnar/Bruce Coleman; **26–27** Powerstock/Zefa Photo Library; **31** S. Osolinski/Oxford Scientific Films; **33** E. & P. Bauer/Bruce Coleman Limited; **35** John Fennell/Bruce Coleman Limited; **39** W. Ervin/Natural Imagery; **41** Stephen Krasemann/Natural History Photographic Agency; **45** J.P. Ferrero/Agence Nature/Natural History Photographic Agency; **49** Richard Packwood/Oxford Scientific Films; **51** Frank Huber/Oxford Scientific Films; **52** Walter Geiersperger/Explorer; **53** D. Gros/EISLF; **Cover pictures:** *top:* Fritz Prenzel/Bruce Coleman Limited; *bottom:* David Hughes/Bruce Coleman Limited; *globe motif:* Terra Forma™ Copyright© 1995–1997 Andromeda Interactive Ltd.